Pringle

Heinemann
New Windmills

RAINBOWS OF THE GUTTER

Growing up together in the North London shantytown of Archway, Philip and Colette struggle to a future in Whitey's Babylon. Easygoing, artistic Philip is deeply reluctant to face up to the truth behind his sister's hatred of the malice and prejudice she sees stifling the lives and hopes of black people.

But then in a night of horror Colette becomes a victim of the racism she has always fought against, and Philip's dream of a multicultural rainbow society seems to fall apart . . .

Rukshana Smith was born in Birmingham in 1948, but has lived in North London for most of her life. Before becoming a writer she worked as an usherette, a washer-up, a woodworker and an auxiliary nurse. She does not believe in the concept of "teenage novels" and thinks that all books should speak to both adults and children. She thinks that books should entertain, educate, inform and stimulate. Her first novel, *Sumitra's Story*, won the 1982 Garavi Gujarat Annual Book Award for Racial Harmony.

Other titles by Rukshana Smith in New Windmills:

Salt on the Snow
Sumitra's Story

RUKSHANA SMITH

RAINBOWS OF THE GUTTER

Heinemann
New Windmills

Heinemann Educational
a division of
Heinemann Publishers (Oxford) Ltd
Halley Court, Jordan Hill, Oxford OX2 8EJ
OXFORD LONDON EDINBURGH
MADRID ATHENS BOLOGNA PARIS
MELBOURNE SYDNEY AUCKLAND SINGAPORE TOKYO
IBADAN NAIROBI HARARE GABORONE
PORTSMOUTH NH (USA)

First published in Great Britain by Bodley Head 1983

First published in the New Windmill Series 1995

95 96 97 98 99 10 9 8 7 6 5 4 3 2 1

ISBN 0 435 12428 5

British Library Cataloguing in Publication Data
for this title is available from the British Library

Cover illustration by Sean Craig

Typeset by CentraCet Limited, Cambridge
Printed and bound in England by Clays Ltd, St Ives plc

1

When Colette got the chicken-pox, she refused to let Ma put Calomine on her spots. Sitting rigid on the bed, she clutched her faded blue nightdress to her chest, eyes tightly closed and her hair sticking out round her thin poxy face. She looked like a zealot about to be martyred. "Calomine's pink," she said hoarsely, "and I'm black! When they start making black Calomine, you can put it on me."

"Don't be so fussy, child!" Ma scolded in the voice she used for difficult patients. "It won't show. It will sink into your skin and won't notice."

Colette opened one eye slightly and, seeing that Ma was not going to attack her, relaxed a little. "*I* will notice," she stated firmly, scratching at a spot on her forehead. "All them lotions and things, they're always white or pink!"

Ma smacked Colette's hand away from her face. "I don't know why the girl's so faastie," she sighed. "So long as it makes you better, who cares what colour Calomine is?" The lotion dried on the wad of cotton-wool as Ma, with a pink smudge on her arm, stood there, not knowing what to do.

"I care!" Colette had tensed up again and was glaring at Ma. Ma relented. "I'll get some Dettol instead." Dettol was acceptable, Colette decided. It was colourless. Ma dabbed my sister's back and chest with the antiseptic.

"Ow, it hurts!" Colette complained.

"Calomine wouldn't have hurt!" Ma retorted, smiling.

"But Calomine is pink and I'm . . ."

"That's enough, now," snapped Ma, screwing the top back on to the bottle. "Lie down and rest – I'll get you some orange juice. I suppose you'll drink that, although it's orange!"

Colette lay back on the lumpy pillow, pretending not to hear.

While this scene was taking place, I had been sketching the agony of Saint Colette on the back of an old paper bag. Glad to get a week off school to practise drawing, I'd let Ma anoint me with pink Calomine without a second thought. Ma looked round and told me to fill the kettle. "I've got to go soon, Philip – I'll leave supper warming on the cooker." Following her out, I put on the kettle. "Now, don't let the rice burn – when Colette wakes up, see if she'll have some. Luckily it's brown rice!" She took her old coat from the peg and went to have a look at the invalid. "She's sleeping." Ma sounded thankful. "I don't know what gets into her sometimes!" Shaking her head, she went down the stairs, humming a Spiritualist hymn.

In the bin there was an empty cornflakes' packet. I slit open the cardboard container and went back into the bedroom. Colette wasn't often still enough for me to draw her. I sat near the bed, studying her face with its broad cheekbones, the brown skin smooth and soft and shining, the small wide nose and generous blue-red mouth. Her springs of curls, black on the pillow, lay tight with energy and anger, even while she was asleep and ill. I still have that sketch made on the inside of a Kelloggs packet. Someone, not so long ago, offered me an enormous sum of money for it, but there are some things that cannot be bought.

2

Just as I was putting the final shading around the eyes, Colette awoke and sat bolt upright. "Philip, the house is burning down!" Dropping my pencil, I tore out of the room and snatched the smoking pan off the gas. "It's OK," I called to her. "You'll be pleased to know that you're having black rice for tea!" I heaped our plates high with the rice, putting most of the blackened portion on my sister's plate. She gamely ate it up, helping it down with huge gulps of orange juice. I was used to Colette getting angry and making dramatic statements; she'd been doing so all my life. Colette and Ma were always involved in battles, with Colette protesting and challenging, and Ma explaining and accepting. They could not understand each other, and I, who thought I understood them both, sat quietly by the side and drew their struggles.

Carrying the plates to the sink, I scraped the remaining rice into the bin and filled the burnt pan with water. I cut an apple in half and took it back, giving Colette her share. "I'm going to watch 'Match of the Day' in ten minutes," I said, stretching lazily and thinking with pleasure of the evening before me.

"No you're not! I want you to help me!"

"But I want to watch telly!" I protested. Colette got out of bed and stood over me. There was no point in trying to argue with her, Ma never won and I was only a kid brother, but I tried once more. "Ma said you've got to stay in bed."

"Cho, come on, I'll go to bed when I've done this. Get me some chocolate powder, will you. I've had an idea."

Interested now, I fetched the powder. Colette poured it into a bowl and added water, mixing this to a smooth cream. Then, to my amazement, she put in some Calomine lotion. The mixture was then tipped back into the Calomine bottle. "There!" she said triumphantly. "Brown Calomine." She dabbed it over her spots. "See, it doesn't show!"

Pleased with her success, she relented and let me watch the rest of the match. Arsenal was playing Spurs, and Arsenal won with two stunning goals by George Best, so I went to bed happy, not knowing what Colette had in store for me while we were convalescing. Ma was working evening shifts that week, and every night after she'd left for work, my ingenious sister made me wash out yoghurt pots, margarine tubs, spice containers. While I did this, she lay in bed and lectured me. "Germolene is pink. Nivea is white. Savlon is white. Talcum powder is white. Soap is white . . ."

"Sometimes it's yellow or green or . . ."

"Shut up. I'm trying to explain to you. Why are all them creams white or pink?"

I tried to think of an explanation. "Because white is clean. You know, you can see dirt on white things . . ."

She pounced. I might have known that I'd say the wrong thing. "And who told you that white is clean? Who says that black is dirty? Can't you get white dirt? You can have white dust and whitish mud and pink stains from ice-cream." .

"You can have chocolate ice-cream, too," I objected.

"Philip, don't you see!" she cried in exasperation. "All those creams are white and pink to match Whitey's skin!"

"I don't understand what you make such a fuss about. Like Ma said, they rub in easy and don't show."

"It's the principle that matters," she insisted. "The person who invents black antiseptics is on to a winner. And I've done it. I want you to paint all them pots and label them in your best lettering. You want to be an artist, don't you? I'm giving you your first

4

job. Get on with it!" I thought sadly about a James Bond film that was showing on ITV, but I gave in. There'd be no peace if I didn't obey her. It was awful being the younger brother. Ma, who was a Ward Sister at the Whittington Hospital, often worked night duty, so I was left alone with Colette. She was a bossy girl, bigger and stronger than me. "Come on now," she persuaded, "I'll give you 10p on credit for some sweets. We've got to get them finished, so I can sell them at school next week."

She swung herself out of bed and began mixing chocolate spread and Nivea cream, Anne French cleansing lotion and cocoa, Savlon and Bisto gravy powder. The gravy mixture curdled and she had to throw that batch away. I was pleased. Maybe now I could watch the second part of the film. But of course she didn't give up. "Give me your charcoal stick." "Not my charcoal stick! I bought it with my own money – I have to practise with it!" She grabbed it from my box and started grating it with the kitchen knife. "I'll tell Ma!" I yelled. "Then I'll tell Ma about them dirty books you read. She'll take the strap to you." Colette had never believed that I had to study the naked form in order to paint properly, and I didn't think that Ma would understand either. I sacrificed my charcoal stick and watched Colette mixing talcum powder with charcoal. The talcum turned grey. "That's all right," she decreed. "It's the packaging that counts."

She went on stirring like an obeah-woman, mixing lotions and colourings together. When I'd finished the pots, she made me paint sticking plasters brown. I had a vague idea that dressings were supposed to be sterile, but knew better than to mention this. Perhaps one of her schoolfriends would get infected and have to have an arm or leg cut off. This thought worried me for a bit, until I realized that as an under-

5

age and unwilling accomplice I could plead innocence. The idea of Colette going to prison for years, leaving me free to watch television and draw, filled me with delight.

I was really a very naïve sort of boy. I knew, because it was impossible to be black in Britain and not know, that there was a great gulf between ethnic minorities and the establishment: police harassment, discrimination and, more than that, the feeling of powerlessness, that even if we rioted and fought and screamed, the whites would still end up by controlling us. But none of these things had affected me personally. My sense of self was so strong, even then, that I truly believed that if I knew my own worth, others would know it too. And I had this magic gift that few others possess, the ability to draw accurately and put down on paper a house, a face, to translate reality into a few pencil lines upon a page. It was frightening in a way. It often seemed to me like a sort of *ju-ju*, a spell, by which I could capture my friends and enemies and make them stand in whatever pose I, the great Philip Browne, decreed.

Colette was completely different. She had been born angry, Ma said, frightening the midwife with her loud furious screech, and she had gone on getting angrier with each passing day. It was as if, with her first breath, Colette had drawn into herself a sense of all the hatred and injustice that had been meted out to her brethren in the past and that she expected to encounter in the future. She scowled at our white neighbours, and they in turn frowned back at her, whereas I, in my simplicity, smiled at them. In fact, I was sorry for them. They seemed to lack the richness and completeness that I saw in Ma's strong black arms. I imagined that our pale compatriots envied us, and I saw this borne out every summer when they sat in their yards, anointing themselves with oil and

6

trying to get brown like me. I smiled at people and they smiled back.

I thought that Colette was asleep in bed. She had given me the last consignment of grey talcum powder to label Dusky Dreams. It was a typical April afternoon. Showers beat reggae on the window, interspersed with sunny riffs. Suddenly a crash followed by a cry made me jump up, grabbing the iron bar that I kept beneath my couch. I rushed into the kitchenette. Colette was standing in the middle of the room with a basket of potatoes up-ended at her feet. "What the hell are you doing?" I shouted at her, my heart thudding. "I thought you were a burglar!" A potato scuttled like a mouse under the table. She looked at me foolishly.

"I was trying to walk with a load on my head."

"You're always walking with a load on your head!" I told her crossly. "I never knew anyone else so full up with troubles. What do you want to carry a sack of spuds on your head for? You think you're a market woman in Kingston or something?"

To my astonishment she sat down suddenly on the floor, cupping her face in her hands. "I don't know what to think I am," she said tearfully. "I feel robbed, you know, and I've been given nothing in return. I just wanted to see if I could carry goods in a natural way, like in Africa, like I would have done in Africa." She sniffed. I started to retrieve the potatoes from the floor.

As I stood up, I glanced out of the window. A rainbow was stretching behind the mouldering houses, lightening the sky with a faint newness. "Look, Colette!" I said, pulling her to her feet. "Look out of the window!"

She opened the window, propping a stick beneath it because the sash-cord had rotted through. We leaned out together, resting our arms on the sill,

7

silently enjoying the unusual peace. The air was still fresh and untainted after the rain. I tried to cheer her up. "See how beautiful the rainbow is. It's a good luck sign. And look, I've just thought. It's made up of many colours, from pale pink to deep violet, all merging into one another."

I wanted her to share my view of the world. I've always had an artist's eye for colour; fascinated rather than threatened by the different skin tones around me. Daily I saw people with almost flake-white flesh, others with ivory faces, shading through to umber, burnt Sienna, Vandyke brown, mahogany, caramel. Ma was burnt Sienna with copper high-lights, Colette was Vandyke brown, I was oak. The different colours of the population were a gift to me, and I thought that it must be really boring to live in a montone area where everyone was black or white or brown. But Colette hated anyone who wasn't black.

She was calm for a moment, smiling wistfully at what I'd said. I felt cleansed, almost triumphant – maybe she would see things my way for a change. Then she turned to me, and said with a savage smugness: "There's one thing missing from your rainbow, little brother. I don't see no black!"

Our convalescence came to an end. The last scab dropped off and we were pronounced fit by the doctor. The evening before we were due to go back to our schools, Colette collected all her medications together and packed them carefully into two carrier bags. I sat at the table drawing as she told me yet again about the importance of having brown ointments. Then she fell silent and watched me, brooding like a queen who has lost a country. I never knew if she approved or disapproved of what I did. I often wondered if she thought that I was wasting my time, but sketching was something I did almost involuntarily. I wasn't sure myself where the cartoons that appeared on the paper came from. I felt Colette's sorrow and anger, and the feeling ran through my pencil and was cast out on the page.

We set off to school the next morning, Colette smelling like a combination of a chemist's and a sweetshop, and I with my battered satchel covered with football stickers. "Hallo, Chocolate Drop!" someone yelled from over the opposite pavement. "Get lost, Peppermint Cream!" I shouted back. A juggernaut lorry roared by, drowning our cries. This was the only sort of harassment I had experienced, up until that time. Someone would call me a black baboon; I would call them a white ape. I knew that I was not a baboon; my assailant knew he was not an ape. What I didn't know then was that some people, because of my colour, truly believed that I *was* a baboon. The terms black and white amused me by their inadequacy. Artistically, I saw so many shades within colours that to speak of people being black or brown or white or yellow seemed a mad childlike simplification.

Although I wasn't bothered by name-calling, some of the other pupils in the school were intolerably hurt. I'd once found Enoka sobbing in the corner because Tony had punched her and called her "Blackie!"

"Let's tell Miss Evans," I'd said, putting my arms round her.

Through her sniffles she explained that Miss Evans always said, "Never mind, dear. Run along and play with someone else."

"How often does he hit you?" I asked her.

"Every day!"

"You should tell your mum."

"I told her, and she did see Miss Evans once, but Miss Evans didn't believe it. Mum says she can't keep complaining or the teachers will think we've got a chip on our shoulder."

Enoka wasn't the only child I'd found tearful and humiliated, but the Headmaster proudly believed that our school was a perfect model of racial harmony. Since he was busy and tall and white, he was able to believe what he liked.

I had organized some of the bigger children, black and brown and white, into an unofficial vigilante playground group, and we quickly put a stop to any racial incidents which involved teasing or beating up. Our methods were simple and effective: we used our combined strength to twist bigoted arms and smack prejudiced heads.

I was welcomed back that day by my friends. Luke

10

took his chewing-gum out of his mouth and gave me half. Danny chose me for his football team at break.

Before we could go into the playground after our first lesson, however, I was summoned to the Staff-room by Mr Collins, the Head of Art. He gave me some kind of test and asked me to wait while he checked it over. Gravely he told me that I had an IQ of 160. I tried to look sorry, thinking I'd done something wrong. His light pink skin flushed slightly, and I stared at the hairs sprouting from his ears, mentally turning them into flames. "This means that you're a genius, Philip," he said solemnly.

"I don't want to be a genius, Mr Collins, I want to be an artist."

He smiled. "There's no reason why you can't be both. You've been getting lazy and careless with your work, probably because you're bored. Now you're better, I'm going to give you much harder work than you've been getting. You can take it home and finish it there."

Thinking back, I see that Mr Collins must have been an exceptional teacher. He could have dismissed my laziness and mischief as typical black stupidity, or as the jungle mentality which many teachers then attributed to black children, taking the label to be a slur, not a compliment. But instead of allowing me to fritter away my time, he realized that, far from being of low intelligence, I was gifted; instead of making excuses for what a sociologist would have called my deprived background, he gave me a challenge, an opportunity.

I certainly didn't feel grateful at the time. I didn't want to be a genius, especially if it meant writing essays and researching projects, when I could have been out playing football with Danny and Luke.

I went home sadly that afternoon. Ma was out and the house was empty. Looking out of the window, I

11

saw no rainbows – only a newly painted Keep Britain White sign on the hoarding nearby. That would make Colette mad when she got back. I stared glumly at the words, trying to feel anger but instead looking at the poor workmanship and the splodged paint. I would have written NF in Gothic letters. The message in front of me was almost illegible. I was a genius, outside of colour, of norms, of rules, alone and isolated in a world of averages.

This discovery that I was different from my friends, not because I was black, but because I was talented, upset me. I expected everyone to do all the things that I did, to draw, to make images, to find associations in unrelated incidents. As I became aware that this was not so, I felt a sense of loneliness which frightened me.

The door banged. I braced myself for Colette's tirade against the Fascists and Nazis who had painted the sign on the hoarding. "Here you are, Phil!" she shouted happily, her cheeks glowing bronze in the sunlight splashing through the sooty window. She held out some money. "£2.20. I sold all the pots and we've got repeat orders. Denton says could we do some black bandages. This is yours. Take it and buy as much charcoal as you want!"

She patted my head and then, in a rare moment of gaiety, dragged me around the room in a Shango dance. As I slipped from her grasp, I no longer felt so alone. Colette was a genius too.

3

We lived in a shanty town off the Archway Road. Litter lay deep on the ground, discarded furniture was left on pavements till it disintegrated or was removed by the needy. Gangs of children and packs of dogs ran scavenging in the rubbish, urinating in passageways and outside homes. On hot summer's days the stench rose up and covered the neighbourhood with a stinking haze, and we had to pick our way carefully through the heaps of canine excrement, broken glass, tin cans and empty packets that are found in shanty towns all over the world, from West Kingston to London. Many of the houses were boarded up, windows leaning blindly to the street, or occupied by squatters.

I loved the area, it was exciting, dangerous, menacing, but Ma hated the constant dirt and noise and smell. This was always happening to me: something that I found interesting or beautiful, others would find objectionable. Once I pointed out with wonder the greenish mould on our kitchen ceiling and the damp condensation runnels on the walls which together formed a kind of tree. Ma, who was cooking at the time, frowned, tapping her loose sandal on the bare floor. "I must tell the landlord next time he comes. It's a scandal the state this place is in, what with all the money we pay for rent!" She went on stirring the stew, but with a faster rhythm, her sandal beating double time in annoyance. Her face was tired and worn, and her brown black arms went round and round. The light played like music over her skin.

"Ma, don't you like the shape of it?" I asked in astonishment.

She turned and looked down at me with her warm sudden smile. "Stop bothering me, Philip," she said. "Draw me a picture of the shape, if you like."

I did what she suggested, sketching her standing in a tropical landscape with a mango tree growing over her head, vigorously stirring a saucepan on an enormous modern stove. As I drew, I wondered what this thing was that separated me from my acquaintances. I could find saints in stains, dragons in cracked plaster, legends in peeling wallpaper. Where they saw squalor, I saw romance.

Sometimes, when Ma had an evening off, she prepared a special tea with some Caribbean delicacy, *ackee* or patties with pepper sauce, and told us stories of life in Jamaica, or JA, as she called it. We sat, relaxed, around the rickety table which we'd rescued from the streets below, safe and warm in the tiny kitchen, while our mother's face became alive with memories. Falling into her old dialect, she spoke of childhood in the slums of Kingston and of the hillside where her father had once owned a plot of land. She recalled the markets and the heat and the rain, the terrible poverty that had forced my father and her to emigrate. Sometimes she related Anancy stories or the excitement of a Kumina ceremony. As she spoke of the magic of the obeah-man and the powers of the myal-woman who lived in a shack in the Jungle, of love potions and curses and spells, the noise of the traffic hurtling down the Archway Road faded away and became a distant drum.

Ma had exchanged a slum in West Kingston for a slum in North London. Dazzled and duped by advertisements promising a better life with full employment, my parents, along with thousands of others, had sailed away to England to be swallowed up by hospitals, kitchens, factories, the London Underground, to be hidden beneath the earth, behind the scenes. My father had found work as a platform sweeper on the Northern Line and Ma trained as a nurse, and they stayed, not content but hopeful that their children would have a stake in the future. For years they worked uncomplainingly, trying to keep a low profile and pretending not to notice their daily humiliations.

Ma told of days spent wearily tramping the streets, searching for accommodation. Some ROOM TO LET cards in newsagents stated plainly: NO DOGS, NO COLOUREDS. Others simply gave the address, but when my parents called to see the room they found it had suddenly become occupied, even if they'd phoned up only five minutes before their visit and been told it was still vacant. There were days when, despite her love for her Mother Country, Ma wished that she'd never left Jamaica, the sun and the blue sea and sky.

Eventually she'd contacted an old friend, who offered her lodgings. "I bet she charged you the earth!" Colette interrupted. "I don't like Aunt Hanna." Ma sighed. "If you'd lived in hostels for weeks like your pa and me, you'd have been grateful to pay anything for a room. Aunt Hanna's been a good friend to me, and don't you forget it!"

I kicked Colette under the table, wanting Ma to go on with her stories. She was getting to the part I liked, the bit where Colette and I appeared. Colette had spent the first few years of her life in Aunt Hanna's "palace", as she called it. Just before I was born, my dad was killed at work – he touched a live cable and died of burns and shock. Ma was offered a

Ward Sister's post at the Whittington Hospital and we moved into our Victorian shack, with little hope of being rehoused by the Council because, as they said, we already had somewhere to live. So most of Ma's wages went on the exorbitant rent for a two-roomed flat with a kitchenette, and no hot water. This last never bothered me – I found it a good excuse for not bathing as often as Ma said I should – but Colette went on and on about exploitation, whites forcing black tenants to live in primitive conditions and then calling us filthy, etc, etc. Almost the only time Colette was quiet was when Ma was yarning about the good old days; then she would lean forward, looking wistful as though she was yearning for something.

Ma, to Colette's annoyance, always took great care of her appearance when Aunt Hanna came to visit us, shaking out her best Sunday dress and hanging it up to air, straightening the curl out of her hair. Ma had the large sturdy body of a peasant woman with broad shoulders and large hands; Colette and I took after her in height, although Colette was slim. Aunt Hanna was thin and delicate and smart. This was due, she claimed, to her royal Ashanti blood. Her husband Eustace was involved in mysterious business deals that paid for her fashionable outfits. Coming from Brixton, she tended to treat Archway as a rural village and us as country bumpkins. Colette would always disappear when Aunt Hanna arrived, muttering, "I don't traffic with no royalty!" while I would be presented with a pound note, stolen from goodness knows where, and sent out to the cinema so that Ma and Aunt Hanna could settle down to a gossip.

It had become a habit for us to stay overnight at Aunt Hanna's after Carnival each year. Their house was large and dilapidated, and they let out the upper

16

floors with a family in each room. Colette threatened under her breath to report Eustace to the Health Minister for overcrowding, but she never did, of course, knowing that these families had nowhere else to go. She usually refused to accompany us on these visits, and I would be sent out with Dave while the two women prepared the evening meal.

Dave was their youngest son, a ten-year-old sophisticate. As soon as we were in the streets, he would draw a packet of cigarettes from his pocket and offer me one, sneering at me when I refused to smoke. He boasted about the number of times he'd been suspended from school, and was hailed by gangs of young men who hung around outside the poolbars and record shops.

Brixton had the same shanty feel as downtown Archway, but with an added edge and an underlying violence. When panda cars cruised by, the youths jeered after they had passed, shouting oaths and curses. Even on week-days the streets were always crowded with women out marketing and unemployed school-leavers walking aimlessly along. Litter, which in Archway was just a nuisance, was here a social statement – discarded packets, empty cans, jagged bottles, old newspapers, stained sanitary towels, used contraceptives covered the pavements. Some parts of Brixton were like a dustbin from which men and women heaved themselves each morning to go to work, or to the dole queue. Eustace was too busy with his deals and Hanna too occupied with her clothes to take much notice of what their son was doing. When night fell Dave would slip out, begging a few pence off his friends. He'd already been stopped several times by the police and, as far as I could tell, was all set to be a big-time criminal.

Dave made me feel like a yokel down from the hills. His clothes and manner were those of a city slicker. The only time we got close was when he presented me with a brand-new paintbox and asked me to copy a five-pound note. Flattered, I worked all afternoon, wondering what had happened to make Dave suddenly appreciate art. When Ma and I got home, I told Colette about our visit and she looked at me with concern and pity. "Phil, you mustn't let people samfie you. You're so simple sometimes, I can't believe it! He probably stole the paintbox and he's got you forging money for him!" She raged away, stamping on the floor in her fury at my ignorance and Dave's cunning till Miss Simmons, who lived underneath us, banged on her ceiling to tell Colette to keep her voice down.

Relationships between our flat and Miss Simmons had been strained since the Episode of the Turds. One of the more disgusting habits of some racists was to deposit a heap of animal excrement outside black or brown people's houses each night, so that it was the first thing the inhabitants saw on opening their front door in the morning. Miss Simmons was one of these manic depressives and a few weeks earlier had left her comment outside our door for three evenings running. At first we'd assumed the mess had been made by a stray dog, at least Ma and I had, but Colette waited up on the third night until she heard the stairs creak. Then, peering through the letter-box, she'd seen Miss Simmons throw something on to the landing.

Colette didn't tell Ma, not wanting to upset her; when she told me, I laughed. "The old woman must be nuts! Kick it back downstairs again," I said. "Then *she'll* have to clear it up!" Colette took no notice. Fetching some old newspaper, she wrapped up the excrement and put it in a large envelope. Her face set and ironhard, she composed a note to go in it: "I believe this is yours. I advise you to try some Milk of

Magnesia for your distressing condition." She posted the parcel through Miss Simmons' door, and we hid on the stairs to see what happened. Indignant howls came from inside the flat and cries of "How dare they? Uncivilised beasts, they're not fit to live inside decent houses!" Not surprisingly, no more droppings appeared on our landing, and since then all communication had been cut off, apart from bangings and angry thuds.

Incidents like this confirmed Colette in her view that everyone was trying to insult her and do her down, but convinced me that the world was a pretty comical place.

4

Ma put on her big pink hat and her flowered black dress. Easing her swollen feet into the flat open sandals that she always wore, she gave a sigh. Her legs constantly ached from standing all day at work. She called me to her and told me to change the shirt I was wearing because it was stained with paint. She heaved herself up and went to the tap. As the cold water trickled out, the pipes gurgled in an African rhythm and Colette started prancing round the room. Ma wrung out the rough flannel and scrubbed my hands and face clean, then tugged a comb through my hair. She looked me over again and pronounced me fit to worship the Lord. Colette scowled; she refused to come to Church and used the opportunity created by our absence to go to a local Rastafarian group meeting.

Ma set off gladly down the road, her sandals tapping on the dirty pavement. Following behind, trying to keep up, it seemed to me that the rubbish cleared a path to let her through: Grandma Moses parting the sea. Years ago Ma had attended a "white" church service, but the people had been so unfriendly and cold that she declared she couldn't find "no Jesus there". So we went to the Pentecostal Church at the back of Seven Sisters Road, where congregation participation was normal and the service went as the spirit moved us, not according to the order of the hymn book.

Brother Jacob, the shepherd, stood at the front of the hall, exhorting his flock to Praise the Lord. "Hallelujah!" we responded joyfully. Someone started a phrase, "It's my life," and we took it up, our voices getting louder as the chanting continued. I looked around me and saw Miss Eveline rolling her eyes and shouting in a joyful abandon as she prepared to give witness to her faith. I really enjoyed these Sunday outings, sensing a warmth that I didn't often feel outside the sanctuary of the church hall. One of my best pictures is of a service with Ma singing, her body full of music, mouth open wide, the congregation in their bright clothes, responding with a freeness and fullness that I've never heard in a white church.

Afterwards we spilt out on to the forecourt, shouting greetings to friends. Ma went to talk to Brother Jacob about Colette. She told me to wait by the wall, but I could hear his voice saying, "You must pray on your knees, sister! We must all pray on our knees!" I felt sorry for Ma; her legs ached badly enough without having to kneel on them, and I knew that even if all the church faithful went down on their knees to Praise the Lord, Colette would never come back to them.

Later that day Colette got me on my own while Ma was resting. "What colour is God?" she asked. Here we go again, I thought, Calomine, soap, God. "White!" I replied wearily. She pointed to Ma's picture of Jesus which hung above the table. "Where was he born?" "Palestine," I answered. "How come he's got blond hair and blue eyes, then? Who said that God is white? That's a missionary lie to keep us blacks down. Jesus was a black man, you know. The Bible has been deliberately mistranslated to fool suckers like you! If you read it in the original Amharic, you'll find it full of the superiority of the black man."

"Can you read Amharic?" I asked sweetly. She

ignored me. "Your god, Ma's god, he's a duppy god who lives in the sky. What use is that to us? You're letting the whites hoodwink you. It's another form of colonization to enslave you and make you doubt your own worth. The only black thing in your Bible is the Devil!" She picked up the Bible Ma had left lying on the table and turned to the Book of Revelations. "See here, 'God has eyes like flames, hair like wool, feet like burning brass.' That means he looks like us. Look at my skin!" She waved her arm in front of my eyes. "It's the same colour as burning brass, isn't it?"

"I've never seen brass burning, so I don't know!"

She shook my shoulders in exasperation till I shrugged her away. "I'm trying to understand," I told her. "You get so excited, I can't hear properly." She looked at me kindly and sat down again. "Listen, Phil, there's no one else to teach you, so I've got to do it. We've got to raise our own consciousness. No one else is gonna do it for us. Whitey indoctrinates us by elevating his own heroes and ignoring ours, by making his God white and the Devil black. And it's a lie, a lie that sifts through your mind till you believe it, and it colours, literally colours, your opinion of yourself and other people's opinion of you."

Colette found the practice of colouring virtue white and vice black a personal affront to herself. Yet she also saw things in black and white, reversing traditional assumptions. To her, all that was black was good, all that was white was evil. I must have been an eternal irritant to her – I could see mango trees in mildewed kitchens, but I couldn't read hidden meanings in words. Since she'd started at the Comprehensive, she'd become what she called a 'conscious sister', angry with Ma for accepting second best and angry with me because I was still young and hopeful. All I wanted to do was paint and play football. Colette would not be satisfied till she had changed the world, stamped out injustice, reclaimed the rights she asserted had been denied to our black brethren for centuries.

She zoomed through her five years at the local Comprehensive like a riot, only turning up at school when she felt like it, insisting on wearing her hair beaded "for religious reasons" and constantly challenging the white viewpoint of education. The teachers classified her as a rebel for demanding what was her legal right: a multi-cultural education. But, with a group of friends she eventually succeeded in getting the curriculum changed: the Home Management course gave Afro-Caribbean and Asian recipes, the library had books by Selvon and Lovelace, Rastafarianism was studied in Religious Instruction and Swahili taught in Modern Languages. She dismissed her efforts, saying, "Well, that don't change nothing. We may know more about our roots, but we still can't get jobs or decent housing!", but I knew she was secretly pleased with what she'd achieved. Colette had decided not to drop out. She was convinced that this was what Old Whitey wanted her to do, to disappear at the back of the class with other pupils who felt themselves to be dispossessed. She wouldn't give him the satisfaction of that.

Colette closed the Bible and went to fill the kettle. The pipes started up a drum solo again and she clicked her tongue angrily. "No wonder we got such a good sense of timing," she said. "It's our environment!" I marvelled at Colette's intense fury, wondering why she wasn't happy like me. Despite beginning to find flaws in a world that I'd once seen as perfect, I was still contented at home and school, although I didn't want to leave the Juniors where I was a big black fish in a little multi-coloured pond.

5

The months stalked by. I was growing up, unwillingly opening my eyes to reality. The first time I realized that the Kill Niggers slogan chalked on an Islington wall meant that someone wanted to kill *me*, an intense shock ran through my entire body as though I'd been shaken by a personal earthquake. I became obsessive, searching each hoarding for its defaced poster. Whereas before I'd simply judged the effect of the artistic merit of the lettering on fences, I now started to sense the madness and hatred that lay behind. And what was happening to me was happening to thousands of others. Just to grow up in a racialist society was to experience a form of paranoia. We all carried with us, my peers and I, the colour of our skin, the shape of our nose, the slant of our eyes, the breadth of our cheekbones, the texture of our hair, like a cross up our particular road to Calvary.

I started to read through Colette's books, flicking through the newspapers she left lying around, and listening to her records of Lynton K. Johnson. I began to react to nuances that I'd refused to notice before. I became aware that although I was generally popular at school, a solid core of pupils avoided playing with or sitting next to me. I asked my sister how I could prove that this was because I was black. She gave me a pitying look and replied that it didn't matter, she'd always gone out of her way not to sit next to honkey kids. "There's people like you in mental hospitals

24

today because there's no answer to that question. Don't let it bug you. It's irrelevant. You stick to your black brothers and sisters, and you'll be all right!"

That was Colette's solution, but it didn't feel right to me. My own way of dealing with hatred was to ignore it. If I liked someone, I felt a sort of buzz, a vibration that told me we were on the same wavelength, and if I didn't like someone, I got another message telling me to cut out. These feelings were not restricted to any racial type. Danny, my best mate, was an Irish Catholic and, beyond our friendship, the two of us had little in common. But some people could only respect members of their own group. Colette was like that. She hated whites, saying that they were an inferior, cold, wicked, corrupt race. Her only friends at school were a group of grave solemn Rastas who spent their lunch-hour studying the works of Marcus Garvey or reading through the Bible.

Ma had great hopes for us. But Colette didn't want to stay on at school or go to university. "I've had enough of The Man!" she said, by which she meant the rules and propaganda of white authority. "I'm going to work."

"Well, Colette, girl," Ma told her, knowing it was useless to argue with her self-willed daughter, "you make sure you get yourself a good job. You could be a nurse like me, or a hairdresser, something nice and steady."

Colette stared at her with horror. "I'm not emptying no white man's bedpan! And I'm not fiddling with no black chick's hair-style. I'm going to be a journalist!" Our mother's face shone with delight. I think she could already see Colette as the Editor of *Woman's Own*, or writing feature articles about children and home decoration for the *Guardian*. Her dreams were coming true.

Two weeks later Colette dashed Ma's hopes by becoming a cub reporter for *Blacknotes*, one of the new black papers that were springing up in London. Though Ma bought the *Jamaican Daily Gleaner*, she didn't approve of blacks getting uppity enough to demand attention in the press. She wanted to stay invisible, out of sight, out of mind, out of trouble, and worried about the growing assertiveness and confidence of the black youth. "Make fire too big – the pot boils over," was one of her favourite sayings. Ma couldn't see that the pot was almost dry. Despite her initial disapproval, I found her once searching through *Blacknotes* for Colette's name. She hastily put the paper down and pretended that she was using it to swat flies. Ma's present was Colette's past. Ma felt that some things were better left unsaid, while Colette believed in documenting every insult in the hope that it would not be repeated.

I moved on too, starting at the Comprehensive, which Colette had just left. Being Colette's brother gave me a certain notoriety; some older students came over to ask how Colette was getting on. The teachers were wary of me – apparently Colette had quite a reputation as a Black Powerite and they expected me to be the same.

I was pleased to find that Danny and I had been put in the same form and as the autumn term continued I began to make new friends. I was one of the cosmopolitans, my mates were from a wide ethnic mix, but there were others who stuck to their own colour-coding. Slowly and reluctantly, I set sail from my childhood shore of safety through the hidden reefs of adult life. I didn't want to make this voyage, just as Ma hadn't wanted to leave JA and our ancestors hadn't wanted to leave their African home, but like them, like all my contemporaries, I had no choice. Of one thing I was certain. I was going to sail my own raft till I found the island that was waiting for me.

There was an uneasiness, a sense of futility, of wasted effort, that hit me as soon as I went into the large Comprehensive. It mingled with the smell of cabbage and sweat and stale air, seeping into the walls and touching everyone who entered. It came from the daily struggle of a few teachers to control two thousand children, most of whom didn't want to learn out-dated theories or techniques for jobs that they weren't going to get. Day after day, students played around in the corridors and classrooms, sniffing glue in the sports field, ripping doors off lavatories, smoking in class, while the teachers talked themselves hoarse.

Normally I sat in the back row, drawing rapid sketches of the disorder. I'm sure the teachers didn't appreciate the aesthetic splendour of the classroom, but it was an artist's paradise – with heads turning in different directions, children calling out to one another or tilting far back on chairs, a game of cards being played with money surreptitiously changing hands.

Futility too sat in the classroom with the prospect of life-long unemployment, racism and the constant threat of nuclear annihilation. None of the students, even few of the teachers, could remember a time when the world had not been in a state of readiness for atomic destruction. The promise of work might have stood before us and filled our waking hours with other thoughts, but we saw the dole queues growing longer. So the school seethed and bubbled with fear and hatred and madness.

Mrs Greeney was a wet. She taught us Geography or at least that's what it said on the time-table. I was sitting in her class one afternoon, busily turning a

27

diagram of the arterial rivers of France into a spider's web, when my attention was caught by the increase in noise. I couldn't hear anything through the uproar, just see Mrs Greeney's mouth opening and shutting while she turned and pointed at a map pinned to the wall. Five of the bigger lads were sauntering up to the front of the class – one of them, a big black guy called Hopeton, casually ripped the map from the wall and, taking a lighter from his pocket, set it alight. The rest of the group, two white lads, two black, produced a length of rope and proceeded to tie Mrs Greeney to the table. It really looked as if they were going to burn her at the stake. For a moment I toyed with the idea of drawing the event. She screamed and begged, while the rest of the class looked on and laughed. The black kids were mouthing her, calling her raasclaat and honkey and Whitey. Morris, a thin, spotty, red-haired boy kissed her full on the lips and then spat in her face.

Something, a chivalrous feeling, pushed me up to help her. I took a swing at Hopeton and he cursed me, doubling up with pain as my fist met his guts. The other boys jumped on me – as I went down I saw Danny come to my rescue, punching Morris full in the face. Suddenly the room was full of yelling savages and burning papers. The thin layer of civilization broke as chairs were flung out of windows, compasses broken, heads cracked and arms and legs bitten and bruised. Some of the girls tried to calm things down, others were joining in with a joyous frenzy. Above the din – it was worse than the House of Commons at Question Time – I heard Hopeton screech, "Down with Babylon!"

Mrs Greeney swooned, which was the most sensible thing to do. The door flew open and the Headmaster, his secretary, policemen and the fire brigade burst in. Hoses played over the flames, the sudden shock of cold water doused the fight. "This is not the jungle!" yelled Mr Merton, the Head, in despair, surveying the ruined classroom. "Some of you should go back to the bush where you belong!" Clifton cheered, pleased to have proof of the Headmaster's ideology. The Police Inspector nudged the Head in warning not to say too much.

Those of us involved in the incident were bundled into a police van and taken down to the local police station. I was pushed into an interview room, where a young policeman exhausted his vocabulary of racial insults upon me. I recognized him as someone who had left our school two years before. He had muttered racist invective in the playground, but somehow that had been different. Now he was here in authority, in control, calling me a bloody wog, Sambo, bush savage and other more unprintable things. This was what Colette had been warning me about. I felt sick. My nose was bleeding and my face badly bruised from the fracas at school. And I thought, a police force is only as good as the society that produces it. If the schools producing police cadets are racist, then the police force will be racist. If society appears to believe that all blacks are inferior and violent, then the police force will be prejudiced. For the first time in my life I had come up against a hostile discrimination from which I could not walk away. My stomach heaved and my school lunch spilled over the floor.

As we were all only fifteen we could not be detained in custody, but we had to go to the magistrates court where Mrs Greeney spoke up for Danny and me. "You wait, Philip!" muttered Clifton. "I'll break them pretty fingers for you. Then we'll see what you paint, cho!" I stared back at him calmly. The bravest thing a man can do is to remain an individual in a chanting crowd. I didn't like injustice, and a bunch of fellas beating up a woman was wrong. Danny and I were let off with a few words of commendation, while the rest were told to do Community Service and suspended from school for the rest of the term. Mrs Greeney wisely decided to take an early retirement.

Our school was now famous. TV cameras were set up outside the gates and filmed pupils going into the playground. Radio and newspaper reporters hung around, interviewing teachers and students. An enquiry was set up and a report promised, and for the next few weeks discipline and education were the main topics of editorials in all the leading daily newspapers.

I had to explain my injuries to Ma, saying that I'd got into a fight. "Lord, son," she exclaimed, disappointed, "you should be ashamed of yourself! Aren't you too old for fighting?" But when she read the account in the following week's *Archway Journal*, her face softened and she clicked her tongue. "Well, boy, it seems as though there are some fights we're never too old to fight."

Colette was now hardly ever at home. She was always out interviewing people, either black people who had made it, or black people who hadn't made it. She championed the cause of Pete Bradley, the West Indian man who had been falsely imprisoned and sustained serious injuries whilst in prison. Her paper ran several editorials on him, and an MP took up his case. Pete was finally released and given a large sum of money in compensation. "Babylon thinks it can do anything with money!" Colette commented sharply. She was also involved in sickle-cell research and wrote articles on the disease, calling for more work to be done into this illness and why it affected certain ethnic groups. She looked into education too, studying the feasibility of all-black schools.

On her rare evenings off Colette would take one of

her Rastafari friends, Ras Peter, to a soul concert or to see a black theatre group perform. *Blacknotes* was sent complimentary tickets, and, if she had more than two, she sometimes took me along. We always made a dramatic entrance: Ras Peter barefooted and resplendent in his blanket and dreadlocks; Colette tall and beautiful, her braided hair beaded and bright, and me trailing awkwardly behind, gangling and gawky like the attendant of a chief and his wife. "Come on," she'd say, "I'm going to show my brother some real life!" What she showed me was real; I felt the pulsating energy throbbing beneath our feet, recharged my batteries on the music ebbing from the drums and saxophone, responded to lyrics that described my environment and situation.

Once we went to hear an African drummer – there is something about a drum which reaches far back into me, awakening a primitive indescribable love of being. Someone in the audience started dancing to the irresistible beat, and then we were all up on our feet, stamping and jumping and responding to the call of the drum. Drumbeats are a narcotic. Everyone with soul has the same response. I've seen white Britons running out of their houses at the *boom, boom, boom* of a Boys' Brigade procession, their children following and dancing and laughing down the street as if the Pied Piper had come to town.

6

"Let the word of man's mouth and the meditation of man's heart be acceptable in thy sight, O Jah Rastafari." Ras Peter took a draw from the chillum. Smoking ganja freed his mind – the symbolic ritual reminded him that, though his physical address was Nelson Crescent, Notting Hill Gate, his soul was in Africa.

Colette sat nearby reading a book by candlelight. Ras Peter had paid no bills for over a year and the electricity had been cut off. He used candles instead. There were wax droppings all over the room, and I peeled a sliver from the cushion on which I sat.

The air turned blue and fragrant. I started to sketch Ras Peter on my pad, drawing him coming out of a candleflame, his dreadlocks singed with fire. He offered me the rubber tube – I put it to my lips but did not inhale. He smiled and leaned over to see what I was drawing. "Put in the Lion of Judah, Jah!" he said. I added a lion, making it seem as though the candle was coming from its body. Ras Peter took the picture and held it for a long time in his hand. "From the Lion comes the candle, from the candle comes I-man Ras Peter. Praises!"

He sunk back and closed his eyes. Ras Ibrahim came in. "One heart, brethren!" he greeted us. He sipped from the chalice and was silent for a while, and then came to sit beside me, looking at the sketch. He smiled and the room was lit up with his sunlight.

Ras Ibrahim, a tall, slender man with a sensitive, gentle face, was an expert on African history and black culture. His locks reached down to the middle of his back – sometimes he tied them in a band or wore them under a tam. Ras Ibrahim had a little room upstairs in which he worked at tooling leather goods with African designs and Rastafarian symbols. He sold these on Sundays at the market strung out along the railings of Hyde Park on the Bayswater Road. He took a draw from the pipe and began to talk.

It was from Ras Ibrahim, the philosopher, and Ras Peter, the clown, that I learnt the ethics that I try to practise now. I was attracted by the simplicity of their life, their concern for their fellow man, their peacefulness. Ras Ibrahim was a true Rasta. Ras Peter was too frivolous and shallow to be a true devotee of anything. I had never understood why Colette went around with him – likeable though he was, he lacked Ras Ibrahim's intellect.

To look back into history for a black person, Ras Ibrahim explained, is to look into madness and desolation: unimaginable cruelty, castration, raping, lashing, maiming, chaining, burning, starvation. To look back is to feel an intolerable burden of pity for black brethren and hatred for the whites that perpetuated these atrocities. Ras Ibrahim showed me how to look back with honour to the great civilizations of Africa. He spoke of the heroes who had kept the spirit of rebellion alive in exile – Cudjoe, Jonny, Accompong, Sam Sharpe. He spoke of Garvey and the worldwide brotherhood of blacks. "Look to Africa for the crowning of a black king. He shall be the Redeemer." Haile Selassie, King of Kings, Lord of Lords was god made man, the Deliverer.

Colette turned a page of her book with a slight rustle. She looked calm and peaceful for once. Ras

Peter and Ras Ibrahim smoked the wisdom weed, the healing of the nations, and I felt a great contentment seeping through me. Ras Ibrahim's words reached like fingers into my brain, caressing me. "Ras Tafari has come to govern all mankind. He is King Alpha and Queen Omega."

As I drew, I thought about what he had said. By claiming the divinity of Haile Selassie, the Rastas not only reinforced the concept that Black is Beautiful, but went beyond that. Black was Holy – if man was created in God's image, and God was black, then each true believer had divinity within him. I had noticed the way in which the Rasses behaved, nobly and with great dignity. Ras Ibrahim walked and talked like a king, and even Ras Peter had a sort of impish dignity. They had turned slaves into gods, and for this the slave-masters would never forgive them.

Outside the house was a tree. Ras Peter had painted this red, black and green, with the initials KOK and LOL at the bottom of the trunk. Red was for the blood of martyrs, black for the colour of Africans and green for nature and hope.

Ras Peter rose and stood looking out of the uncurtained window, the light from outside gleaming silver on his glowing face. He asked me, "What colour is the earth?" "Black," I replied, wondering what he was getting at. "The earth is the Lord and the fullness thereof." I understood. The earth was black, Jah was black, I was black. Like the Rastas, I was willing to stay close to my roots, to work the earth, to sit upon it, instead of removing myself from the source of life, polluting the planet with poison gas and filling the skies with space garbage.

I have never become a true Rastafarian, yet there was something in their teachings that attracted me deeply. I liked the way they rejected the white badges of success: the wall-to-wall carpeting, the holidays in

Florida, the flashy cars, the Savile Row suits or Gucci handbags. I recognized the idea of Babylon, the word that symbolized the power of the state and the institutions which kept men, especially black men, enslaved. Babylon and Rome forced men to become immoral – the Rastafarians were trying to live honest lives in a dishonest world.

The Rastas lived by the doctrine "Jah will provide." Jah, however, was not providing much for my family in Babylon. We were having trouble with the landlord. He'd increased the rent again, and Ma complained that the place wasn't worth paying rent for. She spoke of going to the Rent Tribunal to get a fair rent assessed, but she was worried in case the landlord, Mr Robertson, would then find some excuse to evict us. She had become thinner and older over the last year, as if all the disappointments were becoming too much for her to bear. On her nights off she would sit reading from her old Bible, praying that the Lord would deliver her from evil, or puzzling and frowning over Colette's latest article in *Blacknotes*.

Armed with her faith, she turned on Mr Robertson next time he came. "I don't know how we're going to make ends meet. Look, the plaster's falling off the wall! How you got the cheek to ask the rent you do, I don't know!" Mr Robertson was a small ivory white guy with a big nose and a bald, scabby head. His voice was a whining pain. "I've got so many overheads," he told her. "You're lucky I let you stay here. Lots of houseowners would have said they were full up."

"What do you mean?" Ma bristled. "Don't you say that! I pay rent regular, and we've made improvements to the property!"

"And that's another thing." He swiftly latched on to a weak point in her argument. "All the nails you've knocked into the walls to hang your jungle things on, and those bright colours you've painted the walls. I know you people like loud colours, but if I ever have to get new tenants, they'll make me re-decorate!"

The loud colours were my doing. I'd been going through an Art Nouveau phase and the walls were yellow with orange designs. Ma and Colette had protested violently when they saw the result, but by then it was too late and I'd promised to use sober colours next time.

Ma was forced to back down, agreeing to pay the extra rent. She didn't want to do more overtime, her health was weakened by years of lifting heavy patients in and out of bed, of walking up and down wards, of consoling and comforting distraught relatives. But how else could we afford the rent? Where else could we go? We couldn't afford to buy our own house, and the money that Colette contributed from her small salary was swallowed up in general housekeeping.

Ma had set sail for the New Jerusalem and found it as devoid of fortune as the land she had left, a colder, harsher, more unfriendly place with the same lack of security and prospects. Looking around, I noticed things that I had seen for so long that I had never really examined them: Ma and Colette slept in an old double bed, my room was a corner curtained off from the living-area and the kitchen was on the landing with a plastic screen-door separating it from the stairs.

Ma measured prosperity by material things. This was difficult for me to understand – as long as I could have drawing materials, I was content. But she loved the brightly coloured ornaments, the gourds and bamboo vases she had brought from JA. Sometimes she would stop outside the Co-op in Wood Green and look at the display cabinets in the windows, picturing them filled with her mementoes. Possessions meant nothing to me; I could always find something to draw with, if only a stick in the dust. But Ma felt poor and believed that the white society had cheated her out of her inheritance. She was stunned, affronted, saddened. So she threw herself into her work and church activities, going through our meagre wardrobes for jumble to raise funds for the Little Orphans of Jamaica, or missions to Africa.

Colette and Ma stood at either end of a rainbow. Ma was a colonial, brought up on the myth of the Mother Country, and Colette believed that black people should not see themselves as imitators of the white man, but as people with their own culture and attitudes and pride. Ma was proud to be British, but British society had used and abused her, taking her strength while denying her equality. All the objects that the white-dominated media told her she needed, the luxury fridge, the electric four-hob cooker and the three-bedroomed cosy house to put them in, would never be hers.

Colette rejected these items as toys, white toys. I never wanted them. But I wished that Ma could have what she wanted to make up for the days I had seen her crying with the cold that seeped through our draughty, crumbling house in winter as the icicles formed on the windows. Colette was at one end of the arc and Ma at the other, and between them stretched a multi-coloured covenant of hope. But, as Colette had pointed out, the colour black wasn't there.

7

For some months now I'd been practising portrait and figure drawing. Colette would never sit for me, she was like a flame always darting about looking for something to burn, so I had to work from rough sketches made when she wasn't looking. Her chin, like mine, was African, a proud sweeping line jutting from neck to jawline. I painted her with her plaited, beaded hair framing her brown face and bringing out the brightness of her skin.

Many whites have been conditioned into thinking that black is a dull colour, but it isn't. Some black objects are matt, complete in themselves, others shiny, reflecting the light. Black skin glows with an inner sheen, a warmth. Some blacks have likewise been conditioned into thinking that white skin is ugly, like dead flesh, but I see the translucent glow, the pink showing through. I have freed myself from my earlier pity for my pale neighbours.

I drew Ma too. She was a good subject, always ready to pose. I painted her greying hair, the chin that was turning flabby, her eyes that were brown and kind, yet wary. I felt confident enough to start sketching the kids at school, so I spread word around and soon had quite a clientele. Every day I held portrait sessions at breaktime, either behind the science block if the weather was fine, or in an empty classroom if it was raining. I drew pupils of all shapes and colours and sizes, charging 50p a time. On an average week I made ten pounds – I gave Ma all that I had left after buying a few artist's materials.

Some of the National Fronters came and secretly asked me to paint them. I did think of refusing, then realized I might as well give their money to Ma. And if they wanted me to draw them, they had to speak politely while I was working, even if they went out later sticking up their messages of racism on classroom doors. I drew Denis with his tattooed arm in the foreground, spelling out in violet and red Theatre of Hate, his cropped head and his industrial boots, wondering who this walking noticeboard of macho toughness was going to give his portrait to. I drew punks, Mohicans, New Romantics, Fronters, Rastas – it was all good practice. I drew beautiful Asian, black or white girls and the ugly graceless cropped kids, trying to make my sketches as lifelike as possible. Even Clifton, who was now back at school, came to pose and seemed to have forgotten the threat he had made on the day of our riot.

The pupils who sat before me in the playground experienced the same fears and hopes as me. There had been serious disturbances in various parts of the country the previous spring that had frightened everyone, black and white alike. Yet in a strange way there had been a feeling of pleasure, drama as well as fear. The boil had burst after many years and many warnings, and the poison and blood that had erupted shocked the nation. Britain, land of democracy, land of the free had been shown to be wanting. Various long-held attitudes had been challenged – what was democracy, what was freedom? Two million angry unemployed youngsters were demanding an answer.

I hated violence, but even without a sister like Colette to educate me, I could explain its causes. Our parents had come as grateful children to the Mother

39

Country and slowly learnt that Mum was very glad to see them as long as they did what they were told and stayed where they had been put, which was at the bottom of the pile. But we, the children, had been born in Britain and demanded the rights that our education and expectations told us was our due. We were no longer content to work on railways, sweeping the Underground, in hospitals, as porters, always serving the white master. Some of us demanded jobs as judges, as editors, as actors, as doctors, as businessmen, as bosses. The others, the Rastas, wanted nothing to do with Whitey, The Man, Babylon, the corrupt culture that told us to acquire, achieve, succeed.

While we were invisible the whites had ignored us. The quickest way to bring ourselves into authority's line of vision was to throw bricks through their windows. I didn't want to throw bricks, but began to see that I had to stand somewhere. There was no place for anyone who had not decided. I didn't want to throw bricks, nor did I want my head to be mashed up by a stone. My neutrality was being threatened.

In the past disputes were settled by tribal elders. In places where ancient civilizations remain this is still the tradition. But part of the trouble of the Western world, it seemed to me, was that there were no elders. Confusion existed on three planes: the global, the local and the personal. It was all part of the demonic nature of the twentieth century. Elders had been replaced by annual reports on annual riots.

One day, after Maths, the Headmaster sent a message telling me to go to his office. I wondered if he had somehow found out about my portrait sessions and was going to quote some rule about not using playgrounds as business premises. I went in feeling guilty, but instead of telling me off, he began talking about the progress I had made and how hardworking

I was. Actually I wasn't hardworking at all. I think Mr Collins's IQ test was wrong – I wasn't a genius, just one of those lucky people with a photographic memory and an ability to absorb knowledge without actively doing anything. I shuffled my feet, towering over the Headmaster and trying not to knock his silver cups on to the floor. "Have you ever thought of becoming a policeman?" he suddenly asked me. I was surprised and taken aback. Why ever would I want to be a policeman? "I'm going to be an artist." "That's a pity. You're a big strong lad, just over six foot tall, aren't you? They need big men in the force." He had nearly said big black men. "Well, if you change your mind, let me know. The Commissioner has sent out a memo to all heads of schools asking us to interest sensible pupils about to leave school. An intelligent lad like you could make all the difference in Community Policing."

I escaped from his office as quickly as I could. This man didn't know anything about me, yet was suggesting that I should follow a career simply because I was big and black. I could just see Colette and Ras Peter if I joined the Babylon Met. I had visions of myself walking down the road at night, being jeered and spat on. Even Ma wouldn't have been pleased. I don't think that I was scared. I've never worried about my own safety, and if I'd thought joining the Force was a good idea for me, I'd have done it. To take that sort of step, however, I would have to be committed to attitudes that I couldn't share. To me, the police were just another repressive tool. That's not how they saw themselves, nor what they wanted to be, but that's how they appeared to thousands of black people.

For every black kid, including me, it was the same problem. We were told that we should be in Parliament, yet Parliament was the white man's way of dealing with Government, slow, unwieldy, unworkable. If a black man got elected, he would have to work within the white man's constitution for change, to become white to achieve his aim. Yet without representation, without black Police Commissioners, without black politicians, white people would always hold the power.

As I sketched Ma's soft and ageing face that night while she slept fitfully in the shabby armchair, I thought that nothing made much sense. The men who ruled the world were only succeeding in destroying it. The only elders I knew were a small group of Rastafarians to whom no one in authority would listen.

8

Colette went to live in Bayswater with another journalist on her paper. I think she was relieved to get away from home; now when we met once a week she seemed calmer. She was having some good luck. A couple of her articles had appeared in a national paper and she'd been asked to talk on a radio chat show. The *British Medical Journal* invited her to do a paper on sickle-cell disease. She gave half of the fee to a fund for fire victims, and bought me an easel and Ma the cabinet she had long admired in the Co-op. We were both delighted. Ma proudly arranged her ornaments on the polished shelves. I think this was when she began to see that the direction Colette's career was taking was valid and worth while. She still longed to see the name Colette Browne beneath the Editor's column of *Woman's Own*, but from the way she went to the library and photocopied Colette's article in the *British Medical Journal* when it appeared, folding it up small in her purse and producing it to show her friends and the doctors at work, I could tell how proud she was. It must have given her enormous pleasure to be able to tell the Senior Consultant, look, my girl wrote that, see, Colette Browne. I'm sure that even Ras Ibrahim would have forgiven her that vanity.

Ras Peter ran out of excuses for non-payment of rent and got a job at Foyles, a large bookshop in the West End. Many of his Rastafarian friends had permanent jobs but he saw work as interfering with his meditative life. He found the job satisfying for the short time he kept it, spending his days reading through the books and tearing out any racial or colonial references that were offensive to him. His censorship came to an end when several angry customers complained to the managment that their expensive books had been defaced. Penniless again, he went to live with Colette, announcing that he was going to write a book himself about what it meant to be a Rastafari. This book would hasten the fall of Babylon by bringing the "oppressah" to repentance and thus hastening the return to Ethopia. Selah!

Ras Ibrahim would have made a better job of writing a book than Ras Peter. He had a gift with words, a way of verbally painting pictures. But he said that there was no use explaining things to people who weren't ready to know them. He explained Rastafarianism by his way of life, by the clothes he wore, by his dreadlocks and, more importantly, by following the ideas of sharing, peacefulness, love. Because he was more rational and calm than my sister, I took what he said to my heart – I was so used to Colette ranting and raving, that all I got from her was a headache. But they were both saying the same thing – Babylon sits on a throne made of gold ripped from the ground with sweated labour. Rastaman squats on the earth.

"Where I am is Africa," Ras Ibrahim and Ras Peter said, and they meant it. They carried the sense of their pre-exilic days within them and without them, chieftains in Notting Hill Gate. They spoke a new language. Babylon's language was corrupt, full of imperial legacies that influenced thoughts. It took extreme sensitivity and awareness to speak without offending a black audience, and sensitivity and awareness were not qualities to be noted in white leaders.

Colette said that the English language was racist as well as sexist. Blackguard, blackmail, black spot, black sheep, black mark – even the Bible was full of people being washed whiter than snow, having their darkness lightened, asking the big white god to remove all dark passion from their souls.

It also did not escape Colette's attention that the man in charge of the Riot Squads was a certain Mr William Whitelaw. This unfortunate coincidence merely reinforced the view of many black citizens that the law was white and therefore prejudiced. This belief was reinforced when white rockabillies were given seven years for stabbing an Asian doctor to death, and a black landlord got a ten-year sentence for harassing his tenants. The white law valued property over life, white above black.

I learned more from Ras Peter and from Ras Ibrahim than I was learning at school. The Rastafarians awoke something which had been sleeping inside me and raised my consciousness and self awareness and pride. They gave a new meaning to my life. With my white and brown friends, with Danny and Venkat, Kevin and Guy, I talked about football, the girls we fancied, occasionally about politics. But there was always some secret part of ourselves that was private and unmentioned. We went to matches, met in each other's homes, smiled cautiously at each other's parents, shared cans of lager in the park. They too lived in streets like mine, in shanty houses like mine, but I knew and they knew that if they wished, they had a greater chance of moving out to Hampstead or Chelsea. Danny is one of the closest friends I have ever had, he would have died to protect me, as I would have died to protect him. Yet the struggle I had was not his, and this knowledge was a ditch between us.

I walked the streets of my neighbourhood and I was known as Philip Browne, the son of Mrs Browne who worked at the hospital and the brother of that wild girl Colette. People accepted my blackness or disliked me because of it; I knew who was my friend and who my enemy. Yet whenever I went into a new area I was no longer Philip Browne, but a black youth, and my perceptions were heightened to other people's reactions. I bore my face like a badge, like a black explorer, into homes where no black man had ever gone before, listening for the tone, watching for the look which would tell me that I was being patronized or that my presence was unwelcome. I often wondered whether by the time I had grown up and had children of my own the ditch might not be too full of foulness to leap. I must confess that while I hoped for the best, I sometimes expected the worst.

When Colette took me to concerts or shows I relaxed in the crowd, feeling comfortable and at ease. At one of these occasions, I think it was when a Trinidadian poet was reading his work at the Commonwealth Institute, she introduced me to a striking girl with enormous brown eyes who occasionally wrote poems for *Blacknotes*. Sylvie was very shy and at our first meeting hardly spoke a word, but her smile was devastating. Colette told me afterwards that Sylvie's father had been a black Martinican, her mother a white Englishwoman. Sylvie was a year younger than me and was planning to stay on for the sixth form at her school in Ealing.

In the past I had always skipped the Poetry Corner in *Blacknotes*, being more interested in pictures than words, but Sylvie, small and thin with her smooth burnt Sienna skin and wavy hair had enchanted me, so from then on I made a point of scanning the paper to read her poems. I don't know very much about literature, but I thought her work was good. It expressed thoughts I had often had myself, about self-identity, about belonging. When I got to know her better, she told me that her mother had always encouraged her through difficult times by saying that being black was nothing to be ashamed of, but had never told her that being black was something to be proud of. I knew that I was a Black Briton, quite liking the sound of this; it had a noble ring, conjuring up ancient heroes defending the country from the invader. Sylvie made me ask myself what being a Black Briton meant to me and to White Britons.

Although the girls in my class teased and joked with me, I had never yet had a serious girlfriend. I had fallen passionately in love at the age of fourteen with Rohini – I used to sit behind her in class and draw the sheen of her long black hair. I never stood a chance – her parents had already arranged a marriage when she came of age, so I had to content myself with gazing at her from under my lids and drawing nude sketches of her at home.

My friends told me I was a late developer. Maybe that was true, but I never enjoyed hearing the other boys boasting and gossiping about the number of times they had "had it off" with girls. Looking back, I think I felt that as a member of one group which was discriminated against, I should afford the respect I demanded to another ill-treated group. Years of living with Ma and Colette had taught me more than Germaine Greer ever could about women's liberation.

Although she was so retiring, I discovered that Sylvie, in her quiet way, was as radical as Colette. I found myself quoting Sylvie's views on racism and sexism to Colette on her next visit home, and she made me cross by grinning mischievously and asking how I liked my new girlfriend. "She's not my girl-friend!" I yelled at her. "I only talk to her to be polite. You introduced me to her."

"Look what good manners your son's got," Colette said as Ma came in with a steaming plate of patties.

"Least one of me pickneys knows how to behave nicely!" Ma laughed.

Soon Colette had something else to worry about. Ras Peter was stopped on the street one night and found to be in possession of ganja. This didn't require a great deal of detective work, since he usually reeked of it and floated along as if powered by some invisible force. Colette rushed down to the police station to find that he had been quite well treated, overawing the duty sergeant with his biblical speech. In court he defended himself, calling for a Coptic Bible and informing the jury that they were working for Babylon and their end was upon them. He demanded to be sent to Africa, but instead was sent to Penton-ville, where his dreadlocks were forcibly shaved. At least now Rastafarians are allowed to keep their long hair, but at that time all Rastas doing Her Majesty's pleasure were shorn. "Always the struggle, Jah, always the struggle," Ras Ibrahim lamented. "Sikhs can ride motor bikes with turbans instead of helmets, Jews can wear skull-caps and sidelocks, Moslem girls can wear trousers to school, but the Rastas have to cut their hair!" Sometimes it seemed as though those in authority deliberately set out to annoy us.

We went to visit Ras Peter weekly, taking parcels of I-tal food, which he was allowed to eat because by now Colette was becoming quite well known and the prison governors didn't want any trouble. He came out a year later looking thinner, balder but otherwise unchanged. Pentonville was merely another prison. He had a lot more material for his book and settled down to write for an hour a day. Gradually his locks grew back and when they were shoulder-length he went out bare-headed. With a sense of relief the citizens of Notting Hill Gate saw his familiar figure once again walking down the road, occasionally stopping to read aloud from the Book of Revelations or to shout into a grocer's shop that merchants were the oppressors of the downtrodden. Ras Peter had survived by drawing strength from within. Notting Hill Gate was happy that he had returned and the shopkeeper, misunderstanding his Rastatalk, gave him some apples to celebrate his release.

9

I emerged from school with enough qualifications to get into Art College. Several of my friends were going straight on to the dole and talked eagerly together about what they were going to do all day. Yet to me privately they expressed their fear of the future, horrified by the prospect of perhaps never ever being employed and resentful of a schooling that had prepared them for nothing.

Venkat was staying on for Sixth Form. Danny was going to train as a computer engineer. Rohini was going to work in her father's shop and I supposed that I would never see her again, but somehow, now that I knew Sylvie, I didn't really mind. What we had all been taught at school seemed now, on the verge of adulthood, irrelevant, but I had always regarded lessons as a game, not as a preparation for life. We had learnt the moves which we could use if we wanted our lives to take a certain course. I could analyse novels, recognize certain European schools of Art and Music, and apply a scientific system of thought. As I passed through the gates for the last time, the Headmaster shook my hand and slipped a leaflet into it. It was an application form for the police force. "Just in case you change your mind," he said. Walking out into freedom, Clifton banged me on the back. "See you around, brother," he called, swinging his bag around his head. "Sure," I muttered casually, and dropped the leaflet into his pocket.

It was easy to pass from the routine of school into the informality of Art College. All first-year students had to take a foundation course. This included photography, videotaping, cinecamera work, printing, ceramics, metal and woodwork.

Somehow I'd imagined that my fellow students would know what they were going to do in three years' time, but they were mostly as unsure as I was about the future. Ma had put doubts into my mind by saying, "Look, Philip, I know you've always wanted to be an artist, but painting could be your hobby, like it is now. Why don't you get a steady job, son? Be an electrician or a plumber."

"I'll make out OK," I told her airily. "There are plenty of jobs for Art Therapists or Graphic Designers." But I didn't really know what I wanted to do. Except paint. I somehow imagined that I would continue doing what I always had, recording what I saw and getting paid for it.

Most of my fellow students were exotic, coming to lectures in flowing silk gowns, with long, dangling ear-rings, hair dyed purple or green, or worn braided into elaborate styles. Unable and unwilling to compete with the finery, I wore jeans and jumpers and felt impatient with these embryo artists who talked loudly and excitedly about perspective and scale, or Van Gogh's view of the Universe, or Matisse's exquisite sense of colour. There were some quieter students, and I spent most of my free time with Lynda, a tall girl with tight red curls that held the sunlight, and with Azi, a Nigerian student. I've always disliked those who display their knowledge like wares on a market stall.

Azi had already been at the College for a year. He showed me his First Session's work – it was African in feel, drawing heavily on gods and the tribal carvings of the Benin Kingdom. His sketches had a

51

timelessness that was lacking in my own work. He talked about life in Nigeria and his feelings for the pan-African movement that threw off the shackles of colonialism. He knew many spells and incantations, and he carried this knowledge like a shield about with him. He was black and squat and everlasting. Listening to his careful English, I was aware of a sense of loss; here was the tree from which I had been torn. Yet I too had my own identity which could not be torn away while I lived. I was me, I-man, no matter where I went.

I took him home with me once when I knew Colette was coming to visit, hoping that she would like him as much as I did. The afternoon was a disaster. He found her disrespectful, rude and strident. She found him arrogant and, worse than that, discovered that he knew little about Rastafarianism, only what he had read in the national papers which wasn't very complimentary. Ma and I worked hard to keep them from openly quarrelling. I always made sure that Colette was safely in Bayswater whenever I took Azi home after that. Ma liked him. She called him that "nice African gentleman" and was even slightly awed by the fact that he was the son of a chief.

A few students confused the two of us, since we were often seen together. I was astonished by this. I know that some whites find it hard to distinguish between one black and another, but I had expected art students who were always boasting about their heightened perceptions to have been able to distinguish between a slim guy of six-foot-two with thick curly locks from a short, stout man with neatly combed close-cut hair. I could usually tell an African from an Afro-Caribbean, even one islander from another, in the same way as I could spot a Frenchman or Spaniard or Irishman.

It was at Art School that I rediscovered pottery. I'd

always avoided this at the Comprehensive, partly because the teacher there had assumed that all black kids were brilliant at this, and partly because my only attempt on the wheel had been disastrous. But here we had free range and so I modelled figures from Ma's folk tales and characters from television series with equal abandon.

One of the students in this class, Alex, had a marvellous gift with clay, effortlessly turning out a small masterpiece every lesson. As I got to know him better, I found Alex to be a warm and giving person, a cosmopolitan. We spent one afternoon together, taking photographs for a college project. We went into a children's playground in a nearby park and found some toddlers on the swings. There were two kids, one white, one black, with their mothers. The swings started off in unison but as the force of the push varied they parted company, one child swung forward as the other swung back. Passing at the centre point, they screamed with joy and stretched out chubby hands to touch as they parted again. I focused the viewfinder, trying to catch the movement and the angles. I caught them at the furthest point of distance and again as they passed, laughing and touching. We left the park with the children's laughter still ringing out.

Over the next week, we developed the prints and our pictures were displayed on a cork board for group discussion and criticism by the tutor. We'd all made errors of exposure and timing. I saw Alex looking intently at my stills and asked him where his photos were. "They didn't come out," he laughed. "I forgot to check that the camera was loaded!"

Towards the end of term, for no explicable reason, I began to grow disillusioned with the course. Everything we were being taught seemed so academic, so divorced from reality. Perhaps Ma was right – being a plumber was a more realistic idea. Ma needed help with the rent and I wanted to buy her some of the luxuries she longed for. And there was Sylvie too. We couldn't meet very often as she lived so far away and when we did meet, we couldn't afford to go out, unless Colette had managed to obtain free seats for a show. Getting an apprenticeship might be the best thing – as Ma said, I could always paint in my spare time.

I didn't go to College the next couple of days. I went down to the market and asked a stall-holder I knew if I could help him and was given a job unloading boxes and serving the customers. This was the real world, the market place, with real people buying with real money and worrying how they could live till the following week. It made Art School seem very far away with its pretensions, its self-indulgence and vanity. Suddenly it seemed unbearable to hear ideas that should have been instinctive wrapped up in long words and discussed at length by a couple of long-winded students and the tutor. All education did was to destroy natural intuition and replace it with cold logic, even in art. True art, true music, true living should come out of natural feeling, as the Rastas believed, not from some great learned tome.

I had decided to leave and get a job. I collected up the books I'd borrowed from the College library and took them back. As I placed them on the counter, I saw Alex come in. "Hallo, Phil," he said. "Been ill?"

"No, I've just been busy. Let's go and see if the canteen's open and get some tea." As we walked across the campus we passed gaily dressed students sitting outside drawing trees. "Looks like they're all going to get jobs in the Forestry Commission," I said sarcastically.

The canteen hadn't opened yet, so we got drinks from the Drinkomat and sat outside on the grass. I lay back and stretched in the sun. My back ached from carrying boxes to and from the stall. "I'm thinking of leaving College," I remarked casually. "It seems such a farce, such a waste of time, and my family needs more money than I'm getting on a grant." Alex was silent. I glanced over to see if he was listening.

"It gets a bit heavy sometimes, doesn't it?" he agreed. "But I've decided to take what I want and leave the rest.'

"Do you know what you want to do when you leave?" I asked him, squinting at the blue sky.

"I think I'd like to have a workshop and work for myself," he replied. "I'd hate to get a job in a pottery and make other people's designs or throw cute little vases and make ashtrays."

"That sounds like a good idea," I said. "I want to work alone too, just painting what I want to paint, but I don't know if I'll be able to support myself if I do that."

"You shouldn't leave," he said. "You've got a lot of talent – I really liked that photo you took of those two kids in the park. Up till now I've always automatically worked with either brown or white clay, so that if I make two or more figures, they're always the same colour. Your picture made me think. Those kids, one black, one white, that's the reality. I've been thinking of making some models using brown *and* white clay figures. You could do it too. It might help to change cultural perceptions – change attitudes.'

An ant crawled up the back of my neck and I wearily shifted to flick it away. "That sounds like a good idea," I said. "I suppose I could try it." He sat up with enthusiasm, spilling his plastic cup of tea over his shoes, but he was too eager to notice. "That's what I was going to suggest. Cards. Have you noticed?

There's cards for white people, a few cards for black people, but as far as I know there aren't any for the so-called multi-racial society."

I was quiet, thinking. Whenever in the past, it had been Ma's or Colette's birthday, I had painted a card for them, or hunted round for a greeting with flowers or some other innocuous theme. Recently a black-owned firm had started making cards specifically for black customers, but as yet I had never seen cards reflecting an integrated society. Perhaps, as Alex claimed, it was up to us, the artists, to mould attitudes, not merely reflect them.

"I had thought of doing the Printing Course next year, if I had stayed on."

"Stay on, Philip, even if it does mean struggling for the next few years. You can learn a trade any time. And there's the holidays. I'm getting a job lined up in the vacation so that I can start to put something aside for the future, for when I start on my own. You could do that too. You can earn £100 a week at some building jobs." I lay back again. He was right. I could change more by printing pictures than I could by fixing taps. The day before I had seen a print of a dish of strawberries and cream displayed on the wall. The medium was linoprint, but the message escaped me. Alex's idea was sound; like him, like many others, I had friends of every colour, yet all we ever saw in the visual arts were one-colour groups of monotonous monotones.

10

Exams were approaching. Sitting at the table, I read through the textbook, reminding myself about the techniques of stone-carving, copperplate-engraving, wood cuts, intaglio, mezzotints. "All printing involves two surfaces, one bearing the image and the other upon which the image is impressed." The table shook as a lorry thundered by and the crack in the ceiling, which I periodically replastered, widened again.

I stared at the sentence, thinking that it wasn't only wood and metals that were etched and engraved; society too was marked and impressed by ideas imposed from above. Alex said that Public Opinion was a useful phrase employed to sanction actions taken by governments in every land. The opinions of the public were moulded by those who controlled the images in daily use, editorials in newspapers, programmes on television, the curriculum at school. He wanted to use images to effect change from below.

I sat revising and musing till late that evening, then went to the pub where I'd arranged to meet Alex and Azi. Lynda was sitting at their table, and two other students, Patti and John, came and joined us. I went to buy the next round and stopped to chat for a while to the barman. Going back to my friends, I found them deep in argument, their voices clashing with those of the drinkers at a nearby table who were discussing football teams.

John was a conscious brother. Like Colette, he

identified with the world-wide black struggle. He was on the Film and Television course, and hoped eventually to establish a black advertising agency. "The way I see it," he was telling them, "is that everywhere you look there's a white face telling you what to do or buy. OK, sometimes it's a black chick or guy, but that's usually to do with sunshine holidays or jungle-fresh peanuts. I want to make black commercials, not only about things traditionally associated with blacks, but about all consumer products that black people buy. And that means everything."

Patti tried to interrupt him, but he wagged his finger at her commandingly. "Listen, sister, you know why you never see black folks advertising luxury goods? It's because The Man doesn't think that black people have the right to own them. We're allowed to service your washing-machine, but not to own it. I want to break that wide open, to have a black girl telling me to buy a fridge, or that her washing comes out clean and dandy now she's switched to a Black Power machine or whatever!"

He sat back and took a gulp of beer. John identified the same problems that Colette saw, but had different solutions. Rastas refused any part of white luxury culture, decrying it as the riches of Babylon. John wanted his brethren to share in the white dream.

Patti quickly spoke into the pause. "It's always women who are shown marvelling at how clean Freddy's shirt is, or who serve up delicious meals. We're discriminated against too!"

"You're right," John drawled lazily. "I'm not stopping you from setting up an Anti-Sex-Role-Casting Agency. I just can't fight two battles at once. People have got to SEE me first. That's my first priority."

That's what Colette thought, too. She had told me that black people were made to feel invisible. The way that she wanted to counter this was to set up separate TV channels, radio programmes, newspapers, publishing houses, yet I found this a form of apartheid. But it was true; the images of white society were white images, reflecting what white authority wanted to see. Few newspapers, books, advertisements or films focused on the black or brown Britons or included us in their general view.

Alex lit a cigarette and blew out the smoke. "I think you're wrong, John. What I would like to see is more use of racially mixed images, you know, a black guy being served fish fingers by a white girl."

"Why not a black guy *cooking* for a white girl?" Patti objected.

"Yes, all right, I agree with you! That's another problem which I'm prepared to deal with, but, like John, I can't fight two battles at once!"

Lynda, playing with plasticine as usual, had modelled a jungle scene with a herd of tiny elephants. She caught my eye and grinned, breaking up the figures and kneading them up to start making something else. "You're quiet, Phil," she said. "What do you think?"

"I was just remembering something my sister once did. In some ways she would agree with John. She got a *Cosmopolitan* magazine and counted up the number of models that had been photographed. There were a hundred and twenty-six. How many of them do you think were brown or black?" They all guessed. John thought none, Patti said fifty, Alex and Lynda ten. Azi wasn't listening to us but was talking now at the bar to one of his classmates. "You're all wrong," I said. "Out of a hundred and twenty-six models, a hundred and twenty-five were white. And that was in a magazine called *Cosmopolitan!*"

I stared into my glass, looking at the rich colour of the cider and noting the bubbles that occasionally burst on the surface. The conversation had made me feel miserable. Although I didn't like the fact that there were black newspapers, black radio programmes, black publishers and bookshops, I had to sympathize with their appearance. Yet it seemed to me an admission of failure, even of contempt, on the part of the white society. Black issues had been ignored or misinterpreted for so long that active black workers had been compelled to give space and recognition to black problems in separate papers. The next step would be black schools, black hospitals, black areas, apartheid. That worried me. I also felt that separate slots to air ideas and complaints implied that the white-controlled media could continue to ignore us and pretend that we had gone away. I believed then that the way forward was together, hand in hand, striding to meet the future. But then, as I've said before, I've always been a bit naïve.

During the holiday I got a job in the market and, taking Alex's advice, put half my earnings away for when I left College, and gave most of the rest to Ma. Now that I had more free evenings I managed to see Danny a few times. I always felt easy with Danny – I had no other male friend with whom I could relax so well. He took me to a computer exhibition one Saturday and impressed me by talking to the salesman about binary language and program systems.

"Listening to you showing off just now, no one would ever have thought that you were the little kid who used to copy my sums," I teased him later over a pint.

He laughed. "You've grown a bit since then too. Do you remember how we used to beat up the bullies?"

When I got home that night Ma, looking vexed and worried, was waiting for me, holding a letter in her hand. It was about the Archway Development

Scheme and informed us that all the houses in our street were to be demolished. Ma was upset. Despite all her complaints about our flat, despite the flaking paper and the damp patches and the mould that grew back however often it was cleaned off, it was home, and she had lived there for years. "Where will I put my cabinet?" she sobbed. I sat her down and made her a cup of the mint tea she loved. "Don't worry, Ma," I told her confidently, "I'll find somewhere else for us to live."

After days of fruitless searching, Ma decided to move in with Miss Eveline, a friend from Church. Miss Eveline lived near the hospital, and her spare room was warm and cosy. She let Ma put her prized cabinet in the hall. I noticed how drawn Ma looked as I helped her install her things. "One day," I promised, "I'll buy you a place of your own, and we'll do it up just as you want." She smiled. "Just worry about yourself now. I'll be comfortable here. Eveline and me will get on just fine, and it will make a change not to have to argue with Mr Robertson."

I moved into a vacant room in the house where John lived in Stroud Green. The buildings leaned drunkenly down the sloping street; there was a piece of land opposite owned by the Water Board. Daffodils grew wild there, and, at night, one or other of the tenants from the house would vault the fence and pick some. They were mostly students, either from our College or the Drama School round the corner. Although I missed Ma and worried about her, I enjoyed being more in the centre of things. The room I rented was large enough to set up my easel by the window, and it had a small table to read and draw on.

The second year at College started. Now that I had a room of my own, Sylvie sometimes came to stay at the week-end. She was working in an office and writing regularly for Colette's newspaper. Her name was quite well known in black circles and Afropress had invited her to compile a collection of her poems. She became known as my girl – occasionally we went out with Lynda, Azi and Alex, but more often than not we lay on the bed, laughing and talking. We agreed about so many things – it was a joy to me after a lifetime of arguments. I hugged her to me, finding warmth and strength in her arms.

Colette and Ras Peter were still together, and I went over to Bayswater every few weeks to see them. "How's the book coming on, Ras Peter?" I'd ask, and he would smile gently at me. "Irie, brother, irie, praise Jah, coming along good."

Ras Peter had been scribbling away for months, but I didn't really believe that he was writing a book. I remembered that there was a thin, old man who used to come into the Public Library every day. Whenever I went to the Reference Room to read the morning paper, this old guy was there in a tattered, stained raincoat, writing hurriedly and furtively on large sheets of foolscap paper. "Do you think he is from the CIA?" Azi asked me once, and we both laughed so much that we had to go into the corridor. One morning, the man went outside for a few moments. Unable to resist the opportunity, I went over to the shelves near his table and took out a book. Making sure that no one was looking, I bent down to look at his notes. He wasn't a spy, he wasn't writing a book, he wasn't writing anything. He was simply a poor old man who had come into the library to keep warm and dry and was pretending to be busy so that the librarian wouldn't throw him out. All that was on the sheets of paper were numbers, starting from one and probably reaching into millions.

When Ras Peter showed me the first draft of his book I confess I was expecting to see rows and rows of numerals, so at first glance I was relieved to find that I had misjudged him. My heart soon sank. What I held in my hand was one long ganjascented collection of unrelated words that would be unintelligible to most white readers and simply boring to black ones. "I-n-I Haile Ethiopia Babylon Carnival Mek Fer Jah," was the first line and the manuscript continued in the same vein. When Ras Peter went out for his daily walk around his patch, I asked Colette if she had read it. She grinned. "It's awful, isn't it, but he's enjoying himself and he thinks it's good. Who are we to judge? Someone may publish it, you never know!"

"Colette," I said. "You could be with some real clever guy now. What you want to keep Ras Peter for?" She turned on me angrily. "Don't you run him down, Phil! I've had enough from Ma about him. I'll tell you why I stay with him. First of all, I love him. Second, he's got something which most of us have lost. He's got freedom, an absence of all them things The Man tells us we need." Her eyes flashed, and she looked like an avenging angel. I could see myself reflected in her pupils, standing looking at her looking at me, and made a mental note to use this image. "OK, the book may not conform to what we read at school, but does that make it bad? Yes, I think it's silly, but maybe the words mean something to him that I can't hear. He is ahead of me; he lives in his mind."

She stopped talking, and I thought that she had said her piece, but she went on. "I can't be like him, not at the moment. I can't go along with the notion that the King is going to come and whisk us all back to Ethiopia, or descend and give us a decent society to live in here. We've got to make Ethiopia happen, here, in England, in Notting Hill Gate, a place fit for black people to live in, not made up of garbage and scraps that old Whitey's finished with and houses no one else will rent. I believe that these are things *we* have to fight for. Ras Peter thinks they will come about through the intervention of His Imperial Majesty. I wish I could be a Rasta Sistren. One part of me wants to be Rasta. I need Ras Peter to show me what I could be."

She looked at me defiantly, our eyes almost level. Then she smiled. "Peace and Love, brother," she chanted. "Peace and Love."

11

Reading the writing on the walls, it was evident that there was little sign of "Peace and Love" in the streets of British cities. The messages stated variously WOGS OUT, NO TO FASCISM, KEEP BRITAIN WHITE (sometimes the WHITE was crossed out and BLACK superimposed), the initials NF underneath a swastika, often changed by opponents into NO FREEDOM, DEATH TO BABYLON, BRITISH MOVEMENT, PAKIS GO HOME, the words thrown up from the morass of urban despair. Every day the newspapers told of muggings, beatings, rapes, murders, break-ins. The tide of fear came in till many were afraid to leave their homes or walk out after dark.

Saturday after Saturday fans were stabbed at football matches, coins thrown from the terraces on to the pitch, someone almost blinded by a dart; a weekly Jihad, a holy war fought between the supporters of one side and the others. On the news the football managers bleated tamely, "We don't know what to do about the minority of hooligans who spoil it for the rest." "I know what I'd do," sniffed Sylvie crossly. "I'd ban all matches for a year, and if people still tried to murder each other and wrecked football trains, I'd ban them for another year!"

Although I was a football fanatic myself, I had to agree with Sylvie. I no longer went to matches with my friends after we'd narrowly escaped being attacked by a gang of rival supporters in a tube station. Football had moved from being a spectator sport to a game in which the onlookers participated, often stopping play and spilling on to the pitch to gain a brief second of fame on the television cameras. Bolstered with success, the gangs would then terrorize the locality, smashing shop windows, beating up pedestrians, full of racial invective. Most sane people who lived near football stadiums boarded up their houses at the week-end, removed valuables from their shop windows, and prepared for a short siege. If they had to go out, they went in twos or threes. Peace and Love, brother, Peace and Love.

Sylvie's book was almost finished. She had been writing it down, the fear, in the unique way she had of capturing what it was like to be young on those streets, to be black on those streets, to be a woman on those streets. Her poems told of the humiliation of going after scarce jobs, of being rejected, of being a black face in a queue. Afropress had set a publication date. Like me, she was worried about the black press taking responsibility for publishing black views, but she wanted her ideas to be known, and the white publishers showed scant interest in black people.

"We have different conceptions," Sylvie told me, "different preoccupations. The white government is supposed to represent all its citizens but its links often don't include us. They turn to America, to Australia, to South Africa – in all these lands the indigenous population has been massacred or enslaved. They have kith and kin in the governments of these countries, while we identify with the black, the Cherokee, the Maori." She laughed. "I remember when I was a kid and we went to see Westerns, all the white children cheered when the Indians died, the black children cheered when the cowboy was

66

shot. You could tell who was sitting in what part of the cinema by the applause for different scenes."

Sylvie had shown one of my paintings of a street battle to her editors and they'd decided to use it as a cover for her book. "I never imagined that this would really happen," she told me, showing me the proofs she had to correct. Unwillingly and briefly, Sylvie became a minor celebrity. I accompanied her to the publication party – she wouldn't have gone on her own. She was interviewed for "Black Britons", a radio show, and met two MPs. The publisher made a speech and photographs were taken. Sylvie went back to work the next day, telling no one of her first success. She was happy in her shy, bashful way, yet fearful of praise and notoriety. I ordered the book from the library and took it out on three separate occasions, so that the inner docket had several date stamps on it. Ras Peter was inspired by Sylvie's success to write a few more chapters of his own book and decided to send it to Afropress as soon as it was ready.

I went to see Ma about once a fortnight. She would make a special meal and tell me about incidents at work, patients who had been discharged, or events at Church. In turn, I would give an edited account of my activities. "I haven't forgotten about your house," I told her, and she'd smile back at me, with love shining from her eyes. "I just want you to settle down and give me a grandson. That Sylvie's a nice girl, not like Colette's worthless Rasta!"

She had arranged to spend a few days with Aunt Hanna, so I took her down to Brixton. Aunt Hanna had planned a tour of the neighbourhood, looking up mutual friends. "Where's Dave?" I asked her, and from her evasive answers gathered that he was in prison. Aunt Hanna hadn't changed much over the years. She was as regal was ever, still treating us as

67

amusing guests from the sticks. I wondered why Ma liked her, but she was happy to spend her annual leave at Aunt Hanna's court. When I left, Ma was being shown all Aunt Hanna's new possessions and admiring them loudly. On the long train ride home I reflected that different friends satisfied different facets of our character – like Danny for his happy-go-lucky nature, Alex for his seriousness, John for his humour and incisiveness, Lynda for her eccentricity. And I loved Sylvie because she was warm, modest, inventive and kind.

At Euston a family got into my compartment: a Chinese father, English mother and two children. The other passengers glanced at them surreptitiously to see what the children looked like. Perhaps one day an identical family would not get a second glance, but in this transition period it was hard not to stare. I hoped that the family had not noticed, but they had noticed all right. They had been trained to expect this reaction. I gave a guilty smile to reassure them that it was OK with me. The youngest child, a little girl, came over to my seat and offered me a sweet. "What's your name?" she asked. "Phil," I said. "What's yours?" "My English name is Joanne and my Chinese name is Yung Mei." "That's a pretty name," I said, admiring her light amber skin and glossy black hair. "What does it mean?" She offered me another sweet but I refused. "Plum Blossom," she answered. The train drew in at Highbury. "Yung Mei," her father called. "Come on, Joanne," said her mother, getting up, "it's our stop. Say good-bye to the man." They got off the train, waving to me.

This little incident impressed me, illustrating Alex's hopes. I had given a lot of thought to his ideas, realizing that most of the pictures in galleries or artshops were of white people, or black people, or Chinese people, or Indian people. It was rare to see a picture of a multi-racial group. When I did see a picture like this I felt surprised by the novelty. Alex wanted to make the image so common that the New World would be upon us with its fresh face and complexion. He knew where his train was going; he saw light at the end of the tunnel. Suddenly I felt that I wanted to travel with him. I had been waiting on the platform for too long.

I got out at my stop and bought the latest issue of *Blacknotes* from the newsagent's. Colette had written a feature about a black girl who had gone through the Royal Ballet School and been refused a place in the company, despite her exceptional talent. The principal was quoted as saying, with genuine sorrow, that although the dancer was one of the most brilliant she had ever taught there was simply no place for a black dancer in a white *corps de ballet*. "It offends one's aesthetic sense and our duty must always be first and foremost to the audience." When Sylvie came round later on, I showed her the piece. She was furious. "Would your aesthetic sense be offended by a black cygnet in the chorus of *Swan Lake*?" she asked. "Of course it wouldn't," I told her. "Nor would it offend most of the people I call my friends. Talent is beyond colour. People go to the ballet to see dancing, not to look at the different shades of the dancers' faces!"

We were still looking at the article when John knocked on the door. "Can I come in?" he enquired. "I need a break from Advertising Codes and Practice!" Sylvie showed him the paper while I made some coffee. He exploded. "Well, now, nobody cared that *The Black and White Minstrel Show* offended *my* aesthetic sense," he snarled. "I found it silly and offensive but that doesn't count. That girl shouldn't waste her time on that company. Let her go to join a black dancing troupe!"

"I think she should have been offered a place." I said. "We're living in a multi-coloured society, and this should be represented in all the arts. The arbiters of fashion should set the style, not follow it. Sure, the problem didn't arise before, when there were few black or brown people around, and those that were, like my mother, didn't want to rock the boat. But now we're here in our thousands and the ballet companies, the theatres, the visual media must accommodate us. They haven't in the past and may not in the future, so we'll see more and more black groups springing up."

"Whites see us as a load of bungos," John said viciously. "That's why I want to go it alone. They only allow us to speak when we conform to their idea of us, like that idiot on telly, that comedian, what's his name?" I knew whom he meant. "He's making a fool of us, and we don't need that. He pretends to be Rasta, making out that we all wear knitted tams and dreadlocks, he gets on my nerves with his jungle jokes. He reiterates the white man's concept of the black man. We wouldn't let Whitey offend us, so why allow a tame nigger to do their work for them?"

"He doesn't upset me," Sylvie interrupted. "I think he's quite funny."

"I don't like him," I said. "There are some things, some topics that it's better not to joke about, especially at the moment, when we're living through a very sensitive period. Some people can't tell the difference between jokes and facts."

We argued the point while we drank our coffees, and then John went back to finish his book, and Sylvie and I went out for a walk. We strolled round the streets, at home amongst the black-and-white crowds, passing women in saris, black-robed Greeks, ladies wearing bright tie-heads, swaying their hips as they walked. This is what I wanted to paint, what

70

I saw, and I saw a bright world of many colours. I could not join with those who wanted different communities to live in separate Bantustans. It seemed to me that however unwillingly, cultures *were* mixing. I heard it in the drumbeat of white punk groups. Melodies influenced by Indian and Japanese music were featuring on "Top of the Pops". The textile students at College borrowed designs from the prints of Asia and Africa. It was impossible to live in a city and be unaware of Eastern, African, Caribbean costumes, of other languages, of foreign foods.

We went by a wall on which someone had painted JA RASTAFARI TOM TOM. Even the graffiti was changing, words spilling over from one language to be absorbed into street English. When I'd taken Ma to Brixton, I had seen JAH SOUTHALL HAI scrawled on a poster. I did not see this as a tragedy but an added vibrancy.

We went to collect Ma from Aunt Hanna's a few days later to accompany her back to Archway. Sylvie gave Ma one of the free copies of her book. Ma was delighted and said that she'd show it to all her friends. But she didn't really approve of what Sylvie was saying in her poems. Ma was one of the old-timers, a daughter of the Empire, giving her allegiance to the Royal Family and buying a new dress to wear on Jubilee Day. She would have been horrified and distressed to learn that the Rastas regarded the Queen she loved so dearly as the Whore of Babylon, a reincarnation of Elizabeth I, the woman whose courtiers had torn around the world acquiring colonies in the name of the Lord and Merrie England. She could not understand the youth, black or white. The standpoint and arrogance of her friends' children amazed her, Colette frightened her with her vehemence, the shaved heads and huge boots of the white kids terrified her.

We tried to explain, to show her that we had to change, but Ma wouldn't listen, saying that if only Miz Thatcher would come down "heavy" and clean up the streets things would revert to normal. She distrusted the black movement as much as she disliked the glue-sniffing youngsters and Fascists who stomped around. She was happiest when black people kept quiet and stayed where she was used to seeing them, in the background. I think of Ma every time I see that tactless cigarette advertisement, leering from hoardings over Finsbury Park and Brixton: KEEP BACK YOUR BLACKS. Although Ma resented discrimination, I think she secretly would have agreed with that message. Just as many women felt inferior because their education and male colleagues told them they were, so our parents had been steeped in the language of inferiority. They had been brought up to believe Black Is Dutiful, and for Ma it was too late to change. As long as she could do her job and live in peace, she was content. "I didn't come here for all this fuss and upset!"

She had come thirty years ago. Things had changed. Then there had been full employment, and the immigrants who came were pleased to get any sort of job and somewhere to live. Now jobs were scarce and housing even scarcer. Our expectations were different to hers. She leafed through Sylvie's book again, looked at the cover painted by her son, proud and confused. And so we left her and walked down the Holloway Road.

12

I was now halfway through my second year at Art College and was learning a lot in the Print Room. I went home each night with my jeans splattered and my hands stained various colours from the inks. I have always been charmed by the power of print to reach a wide public and I felt that by printing cards, as well as painting pictures, I could reach as wide a market as possible. I designed screen prints, always with different racial groups featured in them, going along with Alex's idea of breaking down barriers.

Alex lived with his grandfather and brother Matthew in Hornsey, and I began to go home with him sometimes to practise throwing pots on his makeshift wheel. Matthew was working on an electronic project at school, and we often sat round the kitchen table, helping him to insert components. I enjoyed being part of a family unit. Occasionally Grandad would get out his old violin, Matthew would play an organ he'd rigged up out of old electrical goods, and Alex and I would supply the percussion on cups and spoons. These evenings left me feeling warm and happy, reluctant to return to my empty room.

In my free time I was working on a painting of the Notting Hill Carnival, trying to get the feel of the narrow streets bursting with floats and crowds, the suggestion of the sound of the steel bands. I wanted the spirit of Carnival to shine through, this celebration when, traditionally, subjects became kings, slaves became free. For three days the revellers, dressed in beautiful costumes, singing, dancing, shouting, held the centre of the stage, featured on the "News at Ten". On the fourth day the costumes were taken off and the celebrants went back to work or to the Job Centre.

I wanted to paint Carnival as I saw it in my memory when Ma used to take us to the Gate, with the noise and excitement and joyful crowds squeezing through the narrow Bayswater streets. People hanging out of third- and fourth-floor windows, waving banners, clinging to balustrades, bitterness giving way to joy, anger to ecstasy.

This year there was to be a Pre-Carnival Festival in Brixton to raise money for costumes and instruments. Ma had been looking forward to the outing for weeks, decorating her hat with silk flowers for the occasion.

As soon as we got out of the tube at Brixton the atmosphere, ugly and threatening, hit us. Even the drums seemed hostile. Policemen stood at every corner, waiting and watching. The procession made its way down the street, girls in feathered head-dresses, twisting and turning in time to the music, men dressed as dragons or warriors, jumping up and down.

A pickpocket jostled a bystander, a scuffle broke out and suddenly bricks and stones were flying. A rock struck my arm and blood stained my thin shirt. Ma stood still in shock for a moment, then, pulling off her scarf, tied a tourniquet. The police formed into lines and charged, sweeping down the street, truncheons aloft. Ma disappeared into the crowd – I tried to find her, but she'd gone. I pushed Sylvie behind a dustbin in a front yard and we sheltered, as missiles pelted down from the top floor of the house and the neighbourhood erupted into fury. I held Sylvie to me, trying to protect her from the flying debris.

Terror is crouching deep in rubble with only a stinking dustbin between yourself and madness. Terror is wondering if your mother is all right when the streets are too full of fighting mobs to see.

Policemen were running menacingly, striking at random. We stayed in our foul refuge until the streets cleared, then decided that Ma might have made her way to Aunt Hanna's house. We walked back through the broken bottles and blood-stained pavements. As we came up to the corner of Fisher Road, a policeman stopped us. Sylvie clutched my hand. I looked him straight in the eye, ready for a fight. He pointed at my arm. "That's a bad wound, sir," he said kindly. "Want the police surgeon to see it?" "It's OK," I said. "I'll get it looked at right away." He let us go, advising us to keep to the main roads. Sylvie clung tightly to my good arm and tears ran down her face, leaving brown channels in the grime.

To our relief Ma was looking out of the window, when we reached Aunt Hanna's house. She rushed to the door and ran out sobbing. "Philip, Sylvie, I was so worried! I thought you'd been killed!" Sylvie threw her arms around her and burst into tears. "We were worried about you too, Ma," I said gruffly. "What happened?"

She told us that she'd been so frightened when the fighting started that she'd run into a shop, thinking we'd follow her. An Indian family owned it and, seeing what was going on outside, they sat her down in the parlour and gave her a cup of tea and offered her food, which she was too upset to eat. They let her stay till the fury had quietened down and the shop-keeper, unwilling to leave his young family alone with his wife, had phoned one of his friends, who had agreed to accompany Ma to Aunt Hanna's. "He was such a nice man," she wept, "although he was white. He held my arm right through the streets and told me not to worry. I thought you'd know I'd come here. Praise the Lord that you've been saved!"

"Hallelujah!" Aunt Hanna added. Then she noticed my arm. "Lord above!" she cried. "The child's been hurt!" The professional in Ma came out now. She dried her eyes and called for hot water and towels. She was the queen, Hanna the servant. She bathed my arm and bound it up neatly. "We better go straight to the hospital," she said. Just then Dave came in, smart in his two-piece safari suit, his tie slightly awry, but otherwise cool and sophisticated and showing no ill-effects from his recent spell in prison. "Old Whitey showing his teeth, for sure!" he said. He gave Sylvie a wink and a knowing look, but she pressed closer to me, still crying quietly. The women fussed over me and made me rest in the armchair. My arm was aching badly and Ma said I'd have to have some stitches in it.

Dave went out to check on the action. He reported back that the Underground was closed and that there would be trouble that night. The Brixton pavements were seething with evil, youngsters muttering about the fall of Babylon, about burning and hanging and murder. This was war. What should have been a happy carefree day had turned into a nightmare. I felt hatred for the columns of uniformed police stampeding like rhinoceroses down the road, wielding their truncheons on black skin, white slavers quelling a riot. This is how my brothers and sisters were kept down, from Soweto to Little Rock, by power. But this time my brothers and sisters refused to be put down. That night, in the Inner Cities, shops and offices were looted and burned. Cars were overturned and fired.

Since the area had been sealed off, we had no

choice but to stay overnight. I sat in the chair, listening to the screams and yells and watching the flames flare up in the street outside. Dave returned several times during the night, on each occasion carrying a heavy object in his arms. In the morning light I saw that Aunt Hanna had acquired a new colour television, a stereo set, a roll of carpet and several tins of baked beans. She questioned Dave sharply, but he insisted that he had found all the goods in the park. "Baked Beans! You know we don't like Baked Beans!" He turned to me and grinned, muttering, "Thought it was sweetcorn. The Queen likes sweetcorn. Couldn't see in the darkness!" I don't know what Ma thought; she acted as though she hadn't noticed.

I was glad that Dave had been out looting. I needed to believe that the riot had been the fault of the criminal element. I had to believe that it had been provoked by insolence and law-breaking. Otherwise there was nothing to hang on to. There would be nothing between the strength of the police force and my own powerlessness, between their hatred and my hatelessness, their whiteness and my blackness.

Sylvie looked strained and stunned. Ma responded to the challenge and seemed stronger and more vigorous than I had seen her for weeks. We walked to the tube through what looked like a war zone. Buildings smoked and cars lay cremated. Shreds of clothing lay in the roads, policemen's helmets in the rubble. Familiar landmarks had disappeared. We made our way to the Whittington Hospital, where my wound was stitched. I was given a penicillin injection and told to rest my arm for three weeks.

Syvlie brought me home and we sat in silence. There was nothing to say. Eventually there would be enquiries, reports, questions in the House, articles, documentaries. Thousands of pounds would be spent to come up with the stunning revelation that discrimination, bad housing, lack of communication, unemployment and poor education were to blame. But black leaders had been saying that for years. Sylvie and I sat and stared at the Carnival painting, which was resting mockingly on the easel.

I'd often heard SOS announcements on the news and wondered what the people involved must feel like. Next day, as I lay on my bed watching Sylvie cooking a curry on the Baby Belling, I heard distantly on the radio, "Will Mr David Nathaniel Drysdale, last heard of in Brixton, please go to the King's College Hospital, where his mother, Mrs Hanna Drysdale, is dangerously ill." My blood ran cold and there was thudding in my ears. "Sylvie," I called feebly, "did you hear that?" She stopped chopping onions and wiped the tears from her eyes. "What, no, I wasn't listening." I told her what I'd heard. "That's Aunt Hanna. We only saw her yesterday. There must be a mistake." Sylvie turned off the cooker and put her jacket on. "Lie still," she said. "Just give me the name of the hospital. I'll go out and phone. I'll be back as soon as I can."

She was only gone about fifteen minutes but it felt like for ever. I lay back, worrying and fuming because I was so weak. I'd hardly ever been ill before – I come from a tough family who didn't take much notice of minor aches and pains – but that day I had a temperature, my head ached badly and my arm was throbbing. Nathaniel. I hadn't known that Dave's middle name was Nathaniel. When Sylvie returned, she looked grave. "Phil," she said, sitting on the bed, "It's bad news. Your aunt was stabbed yesterday morning. She was going to do some marketing when two young white kids jumped her. She was knifed in the chest. They don't think she'll last the night."

I turned my head to the pillow, biting my lip. When I managed to speak my voice was hoarse and useless. "The bastards! What the hell did they stab her for?" Sylvie held me tight. "It's not the first time there's been senseless violence, and I shouldn't think it will be the last. You mustn't let it get to you – we've got to fight it, this madness, in whatever way we can. And going mad ourselves won't help!"

"Dave, does he know?"

"He'd phoned in just before me. One of his mates had heard the SOS and he's on his way to the hospital now."

"This will kill my mother," I said. "She didn't want to notice these things. But now she'll have to. I never knew what she saw in Aunt Hanna, but they were really close friends. It'll finish her."

Somehow the evening passed. I even managed to eat a few spoonfuls of the food Sylvie had prepared and my headache went, leaving in its place a tightness, a horror that I had never felt before.

By morning my fever had dropped and I felt stronger. "I must go and see Ma," I said. "If you feel well enough, I think you should," Sylvie agreed. "But I'm coming with you." We stopped off first at a grocer's shop to buy Ma some *ackee* and black-eye peas. I insisted on carrying them despite feeling very tired. As we walked up the path to Ma's house, Miss Eveline opened the front door. "Afternoon, Miss Eveline," I greeted her. "How you keeping?" She stared at me as if I was a ghost, her mouth opening and shutting so that I could see right down her throat. Then she burst into sobs and pulled me close. I could feel the tin of *ackee* digging into my ribs and my wound hurt where she was clasping it. I wondered if Miss Eveline had gone mad; sweat gathered on my brow and I pulled away.

"She's dead, Philip – your Ma's dead!"

One second everything had been in focus, now everything was off balance. The flowers in the garden had become brighter, there was a time lapse between Miss Eveline's mouth opening and her words, minutes later, reaching my ears. I wanted to laugh, to roar with laughter. There was a tin of *ackee* lying on the floor, spinning round and round, and little black-eye peas were jumping up and down like Kumina dancers at a Nine Night feast.

Sylvie was there beside me, supporting me and leading me into the house.

"What happened, Miss Eveline?"

"We heard it on the news, about your mother's friend. She looked so sad, I saw the Angel of Death come for her. I felt the cold air of his wings on my face. She looked up and saw him, and all the sorrow drained from her face and she was sanctified with the Holy Spirit. I called the doctor. He came right away and said she'd had a heart attack."

"Where is she now?" Sylvie asked. Ma was lying upstairs, with the Sisters of the Church keeping Dead Watch near her. I heaved myself painfully to her room – Ma was lying on the bed, her sweet face peaceful, a smile touching her lips, the lines erased from her flesh. She had gone to meet her Landlord in the sky.

Colette arrived and, though I'd expected her to break down, she stood dry-eyed and calm. "She'd served her time," she said. "She suffered enough and now she's free." Turning to me she chided, "Everyone's parents have got to die." Colette wasn't heartless, she was simply hardened, toughened by what had been thrown at her. She grieved, quietly, not like the Sisters who wailed and cried and sang Ma to rest. "Everything was against her, her age, her colour, her sex. Do you know how many times she'd put in for further training and been passed up for younger, whiter nurses? Now she's out of it, free." I hadn't known any of this – I'd thought that Ma had gone as far as she'd wanted to. Like Ma, I'd closed my mind to things I didn't want to know, leaving Colette to fight our battles.

I passed the next few weeks in oblivion. I sat in my room without moving – and the nights were filled with memories and dreams. Danny came round once, but I hardly noticed him. "She was a nice woman, Phil, I'm sorry she's gone. I'll light a candle for her." Candles glimmer for a while and go out. Alex and his brother Matthew came and sat with me; John kept me company; Ras Peter held spliffs to my lips. I floated into another time with Ma's voice and face around me. Peace and Love, Mother, Peace and Love. Aunt Hanna was still in Intensive Care, miraculously gaining strength each day. *Why didn't you wait, Ma?* I accused her. She's going to be all right.

The fire at Afropress singed me back to reality. Someone threw a petrol bomb into the premises one night and the place went up in flames. Manuscripts, documents and contracts had been destroyed. *Burn, Burn, Burn.* Black kids poured into the streets, marching in protest. This was an affront. Babylon was trying to gag us. Afropress would not be gagged. They moved into new premises supplied by white well-wishers and a fund was started to buy new equipment.

Danny came round again. "I want to help. What can I do?" I stared awkwardly at him. I didn't know what to say. He pressed £50 into my hand. "Give this to the fund, will you. I feel sick about what's happening. First your aunt being stabbed and now this!" He sat down in the wobbly chair and rocked his weight from side to side. "It's not just here, it's all over. My Uncle Liam has been wounded in Belfast, people are scared to walk the streets – I can't understand what's going on."

I made some tea and we talked into the night, easily, openly, our reserves down. We could both admit our fear to each other and it was a relief to do so. With Sylvie I had to pretend a strength that I did not have, while Colette was totally fearless. Ras Peter and the brethren were armed with an inner certainty. To Danny that night I talked out my fear, and so did he, and somehow, when he left in the morning, my fear left with him. I mounted the steps to my little room and saw the early morning sun touching my Carnival picture with rose and gold. I took a sharp knife and slashed the canvas across and across, till it hung in limp ribbons from the frame. Standing the ruined painting in the corner, I fell on the bed and slept.

13

I didn't tell Colette where the £50 had come from; since Aunt Hanna's stabbing and Ma's death she had become unapproachable, and the fire at Afropress had made her even more distant. The police had questioned many suspects but made no arrests. People muttered that they weren't trying hard enough, that they didn't want to find the culprits. In fact the police were mystified. They had interviewed members of Right Wing organizations and each time had drawn a blank. We were shocked when the person they picked up for "helping in their enquiries" was Ras Peter. It had to be a fit-up, a framing. Colette went storming into the police station, convinced that they were trying to implicate her in some way. But when she got there Ras Peter had already admitted his guilt.

We couldn't believe it; the police must have forced him to make a false statement. But it was true. The story slowly emerged that Afropress, publishers of black people's work, had returned his manuscript, and Ras Peter, equating them with Babylon and as black betrayers of his life's work, had taken his revenge. We went to the trial, his lawyer pleaded his client's insanity and Ras Peter was admitted to a Psychiatric Unit in Hornsey under Section 26 of the Mental Health Act. I went with Colette to visit him – he lay on a bed, resplendent in a hospital night-gown, his dreadlocks flowing on to the pillow. He was refusing all drugs and medication except the one herb that was not allowed. As we entered the ward with our gifts of I-tal food and mangoes, we found him lecturing a nervous white consultant about the beneficial effect of ganja.

The doctor looked relieved as we entered and seized the excuse to leave. "Ah, you have some visitors, Mr Raas," he said politely, and made his escape. "Mr Raas" heaved himself up in bed and greeted us. "One love." I felt a bit uncertain at first, unsure whether he was really mad and likely to turn violent, or if his lawyer had merely found a convenient alternative to a prison sentence. He didn't look mad, but then he had burnt down Afropress. He was talking quite normally to Colette, so I relaxed.

Ras Peter stayed in the Unit for several months. At first he used passive resistance to any psychiatric techniques and sat reading his Bible out loud and explaining passages to passing patients or staff. He would not participate in occupational therapy and, if threatened, would take off his nightgown and walk around the wards. It was only when electric shock treatment was suggested that he agreed to attend therapy sessions, which he then disrupted by extolling the use of ganja over Valium and encouraging patients to stroll the grounds in "natural naturality" instead of doing cooking and basketwork.

After visiting Ras Peter that first time, I had arranged to meet Danny outside Finsbury Park Station. I dislike waiting and kept glancing at my watch to check the time. The pub we were going to was quite small and would be crowded unless we got there early. I gave him ten minutes and then decided to leave. I was a bit concerned; it wasn't like Danny not to show up. I went into the station and found a phone box. Picking up the receiver, I noticed that the wire had been cut through. The coin box had been ripped from the adjoining kiosk. Cursing, I tried a third. This was OK. Dialling Danny's number, I asked for his room. The girl who answered told me he had been taken to hospital.

It was like a recurring nightmare. London was turning into a casualty ward. I got a grip on myself and asked for the address. By the time I arrived, it was past visiting hours, but I was so distraught that the Philippino night nurse let me in for five minutes. Danny was chalk-white, and his head was swathed in bandages. "What the hell's going on?" I asked, shocked. "What's happened now?"

As he tried to speak, a tear rolled down his face. I filched a tissue from the next patient's locker and wiped it away. I held his hand, noticing how cold it was. He began to whisper, and I leant close to hear. He'd called into his local to buy some cigarettes just before setting out to meet me. A crowd of black youths had burst in with axes and hammers and had set about the customers. It had been pandemonium: tables overturned, glasses emptied, axes falling. Danny had been struck on the head and severely concussed; many of the other customers had been injured too. The kids had yelled that they were taking revenge for a black boy who had been beaten up by skinheads the week before.

I felt guilty, although I had not struck him. He squeezed my hand gently and tried to smile. "It's not you and me, Phil," he murmured. "We're friends." We *were* friends. Only sometimes it's hard to stand up and be counted. It was hard for Danny and it was hard for me. For Danny to be seen with me marked him as a traitor to the United Whites. For me to be seen with Danny exposed me as an Uncle Tom. We operate our own closed shops. In that time of redefining attitudes, of sharpening tensions, it was easier to stay behind a barrier raised by history than to walk out into the future. I'd long ago resolved that no one was going to tell me whom my friends should be, but I was aware now of the courage that this sometimes involved. The black nurse who came to adjust Danny's drip gave me a sidelong glance, and I caught the surprise in a white nurse's eyes as she hurried past with a bedpan.

We were living in a vicious circle, with a line drawn down the middle, and on either side of the sphere were ranks of enemies, ready to kill, injure, maim. Some of us stood on the dividing line, trying to hold hands, but more likely than not we were put out of action by a threat or a brick.

Aunt Hanna was released from hospital and sent a note expressing her sorrow about Ma, saying that I would be welcome at her home any time. I knew that I would never go there again, but posted her a card thanking her and saying I was glad she was getting better. I wondered if Dave was still acquiring ornaments for her. She asked subtly in her note if anyone had claimed Ma's cabinet – she would so like it for a keepsake. I was pleased that we had already given the cabinet to Miss Eveline.

It was after this terrible period that I began to draw again. My work had changed, my style was more savage, less humorous. I painted what I had seen. Ma's funeral, mourners clustering round the grave. Danny in hospital with me visiting him. Street riots with black and white youths, mouths open, screaming at the police and each other and hurling bricks. I painted the battle in the pub as Danny had described it – and black children being stopped by the police. I painted it as I saw it, and each completed picture relieved my pain.

I spent most of my days in my room, standing over the easel, painting the shanty town of Archway and the streets of Finsbury Park, the markets of Brixton. Friends came and went and said that my work was amazing. I smiled at their praise, but didn't care whether they approved or not. I was painting what I saw, the ugliness, the violence, the fear beneath the surface. Through my work I was trying to find a place where I could stand, and, as I painted, the words of my friends lamented in my head. Lynda had told me that Azi's black landlady refused to have her in the house, and that her own mother wouldn't let Azi over the doorstep. "Where can we meet?" she'd asked me. I had no answer. I'd once waited at a bus stop and, turning round, found that I was in front of a KILL THE BLACKS slogan. Where was there a place to stand, I asked myself, especially when I wanted to stand with friends of every colour? Where did Sylvie stand, her sepia skin evidence of mixed white and black within her? I hoped the cards I was designing would somehow make a place for us all to stand in friendship, but wondered also, whether I was creating an illusion.

14

It was a miserable summer. I had vivid dreams in which I was back home, with Ma laughing at a joke or scolding Colette. When I awoke, it took me some time to realize where I was; each morning brought a new sense of loss, and grief.

To add to my depression there was a lot of outrage about a proposed South African cricket tour which split the country into three. There were those who couldn't care less, there were those passionately in favour, those who were violently opposed. Cricket to some meant summer afternoons, cream teas, aching muscles, exhilaration; the smell of sweat and linseed oil, the sound of applause as a four was hit, or a batsman caught out. To others it meant the carrying of passes, exploitation, squalor, apartheid.

Those who wanted the tour to go ahead said, "Keep politics out of sport!" But Colette said that politics was present in everything: in deciding who ate the best food, who was fit, who was literate, who got the best training, the finest facilities, and who had to make do with crusts, a home-made bat, a sandy scrubland for a pitch. Those in favour saw the tour as a sporting event, those against as a betrayal. Sylvie likened it to inviting to tea someone who had tortured your entire family.

The Anti-Apartheid Committee had seen the cover of Sylvie's book and asked me to draw a poster for them. I painted a South African Zulu staring out of a prison cell, his face thin, his eyes hopeless and almost closed. The bars of the cell were made of cricket stumps. The prisoner had been bowled out at birth. There were no words; the poster spoke for itself. The organizer of the protest were pleased, and I soon saw my work on walls and hoardings.

Azi returned to Africa. He had finished the course and was going back to Nigeria to teach. Lynda started going out with Alex and some months later they got married. Matthew left school and looked unsuccessfully for work. Many of the factories he had hoped to get a job in as a trainee had closed down and he was becoming depressed and despondent. Eventually he applied to join the Royal Navy as an engineer, and went off to a Naval School in Falmouth.

I was looking for a temporary job for the summer break, so when I saw that a factory in Crouch End was advertising for casual workers over the holiday period, I applied for a post. The factory was a large greyish building, manufacturing self-assembly furniture. Planks of pinewood and laminated sheets were stacked in piles in the covered yard, and sanding-machines and electric saws could be heard grinding away in the workshops. Mick the foreman interviewed me, checked me over, felt the muscles in my forearm, and told me to report for work at 6.00 a.m. the next day. He sent me to the office on the top floor to sort out my cards, and a tired-looking Asian girl filled out a form and handed it to me to sign.

For the next three months I clocked in at 6.00 a.m. and clocked out at 3.00 p.m. The work was so boring that I couldn't understand how some of the blokes had been there for thirty years. My job was to glue white laminated strips on to the ends of finished planks and pass them on to the man at the next bench, who then drilled holes. The planks were eventually to be jointed together as shelves. Every time I see self-assembly furniture, I think with sympathy of the poor worker who has made it. The glue we used was hot, 200 degrees. By the end of the first day I had completed the required total of 3,000 units, but my hands were blistered and raw.

Many of the workforce were middle-aged Indians and Pakistanis, who chattered to each other in Gujarati or Urdu. There were a couple of other casual labourers, Tony and Georgiou, who were also students, Tony at the London School of Economics and Georgiou at Middlesex Polytechnic. As temporaries, we were regarded as the lowest form of life and, had it not been for their company, I guess I would have gone mad with the tedium of it all. *Plank – glue – strip – pile. Plank – glue – strip – pile*. I repeated that motion 3,000 times each day, until my arms ached and my shoulder muscles groaned.

By the end of that interminable first week my hands were weeping and tender, and I really felt I'd earned the £70 in its little brown envelope. "Please check contents before leaving wages office – mistakes cannot be rectified afterwards." We stood, the three of us, counting the crisp new notes with our blistered fingers. The first purchase I made was some cream – I couldn't touch a paintbrush or even clench my fist that week-end. "Why don't you wear gloves?" Sylvie asked, bathing my hands with warm water and rubbing on the balm. I winced. "You can't wear ordinary gloves because they slow you down, and rubber or plastic gloves would melt. I'll just have to put up with it." After a couple of weeks I felt as if I'd worked there all my life; my hands grew new skin and stopped blistering.

I had become a machine. *Plank – glue – strip – pile. Plank – glue – strip – pile*. In a moment of depression, I calculated that by the time I haed finished working at the factory I'd have stuck on 360,000 laminated strips. Surely unemployment could be no worse than a job like this? I had made a few friends among the permanent workforce and pitied the men trapped in this job, destined to glue and saw till they retired so that they could feed, clothe and house their families.

I was pleased to get a postcard from Danny. He had gone to France to convalesce from his injury before returning to work, and the bright foreign stamp and cheerful greeting made me briefly forget my drab surroundings. Two other things helped to lift my gloom. Firstly Sylvie decided to move in with me and secondly I was given the chance to hold my first exhibition.

Colette had connections in art galleries and had mentioned my work to one of the owners she knew. I was invited to exhibit, and Sylvie helped me pick out my best pictures. At the back of the pile, dusty and forgotten, was the ruined Carnival picture. "What's that?" she exclaimed, and I explained how it came to be in tatters. "That's really good! That's Carnival as it was last year, ripped and spoilt. Put it in, Phil, you could call it 'Carnival Ribbons'!" Her enthusiasm got to me. I looked at the picture. She was right. The basic picture could still be made out: happy, laughing, singing crowds enjoying the masquerade. Then the mask ripped off, destroyed, torn. "OK. I'll take that one too!"

The public came to see my work. It was the first time that such explicit street scenes had been exhibited and I was hailed as the Great Black Hope of British Art. They said that I had started a New School, which was rubbish, of course – I was simply repeating lessons that I had learned. "Carnival Ribbons" was acclaimed as social realism of an unprecedented kind. The national papers gave the exhibition space on their Arts Pages, and I was interviewed by a couple of radio stations. But notoriety meant nothing to me, nothing at all. A little adulation could in no way make up for the agonies of the previous year, but I was pleased that all the pictures sold, except for the one of Ma's funeral. That one I wanted to keep.

15

Ras Peter was eventually discharged from the Psychiatric Unit, and to celebrate his release from the clutches of Babylon, Sylvie and I took him and Colette to the Harlem Ballet at Covent Garden Opera House. The mainly black audience was wildly enthusiastic. We cheered and hooted and shouted after each dance, expressing our solidarity by clapping our brothers and sisters on stage. Some of my best friends are white, but that evening it struck me that whenever I had gone to see a play with largely white spectators the applause was polite, muted, a duty. The more exuberant souls were crushed by the atmosphere of restraint. A black crowd has its own energy, a grace, a generosity that makes it pound hand against hand, cheer, call out salutations. And the dancers responded to our eagerness, smiling and waving back so that we were one. The female lead was the young girl that Colette had written about, who had failed to gain a place in the Royal Ballet Company, in deference to the presumed aesthetic sensibilities of the British Public. We knew her story and gave her a standing ovation.

While in hospital Ras Peter had completed a new book that set out to trace links between Welsh Nationalists and Rastafarians. It was called *Ras Beca and the Sons of Negus*. He submitted it to the Caribeat Press. Recognizing his name from the arson trial, they accepted the manuscript immediately, sending a contract by return of post. Ras Ibrahim, Colette and myself agreed that they probably would never publish it, finding excuses until Ras Peter had forgotten about the work, but it was on the book-stands a few months later. We couldn't imagine anyone taking it seriously, and were astonished when the critics hailed Ras Peter as one of Britain's most promising writers and *The Times* ran a three-page centre spread on the book and its author. He was swamped with requests to appear on television and was even invited to speak on "Any Questions".

Colette was becoming well known too, although in a different way. She had always been a fighter and through her journalism was familiar to many organizations. Increasingly she was invited to speak about black issues or talk at political functions. I saw her once at a meeting, denouncing the way blacks were treated by the media. I painted the scene afterwards, Colette with her hand outstretched, making a point sternly but with great dignity, her tall thin figure in an African print top over jeans, the green baize table in front with its cups and water jug, a speaker one side of her, two the other, their faces turned towards her, as she addressed the floor. I painted this in the style of Ablade Glover, dabs of paint looking just like blotches when seen close up, but from a few yards away becoming a crowd. Ablade painted scenes of Ghana, his crowds were black, but I had the advantage of living in London. A market scene, a cinema queue, a crowd at a meeting were made up of black, brown, ochre, umber, Sienna, pink, rosy, whitish faces which I portrayed by multi-coloured daubs. This gave my paintings what the critics called its "mosaic effect".

Ras Peter began to discuss the possibility of another book with his publishers. He suggested a link between the inhabitants of Stoke-on-Trent with another lost African tribe, having noticed that the town was in the middle of the Black Country. The first book had succeeded due to the political climate and a great deal of luck. His publishers were extremely doubtful that the luck would hold but, knowing Ras Peter was potentially dangerous, dared not refuse outright. They suggested a promotional tour of the Caribbean Islands which they would finance. Ras Peter grasped this chance to contact Rastafarian groups and set off from Heathrow in a blaze of publicity.

I began to see Colette sometimes in the company of a young white guy called Jimmy. His face was familiar, and he turned out to be a spokesman for minority groups who had often appeared on TV. Colette was changing – although she was twenty-six she had up till then managed to avoid any intimate contact with "honkeys". I took to Jimmy immediately; he was as tall as me and that in itself was an advantage. I have nothing against small people but it gives me a terrible neck-ache when I have to bend down all the time to hear what they are saying, whereas I feel an easy equality with those of my own height. Jimmy, apart from being tall, was intelligent, politically aware, generous and had a sense of humour. Colette glowed in his company. When they weren't talking politics their relationship had a teasing quality. I had never seen her tease anyone before; she had always said that life was too serious to waste time mucking about. Now the tenseness in her face was replaced sometimes with amusement. "What about Ras Peter?" I asked her once when we were alone. She looked sad for a moment and then replied, "Ras Peter is my brother and I love him. Jimmy is different. I don't know." Then she asked, "What about Sylvie? You going to marry her or what?"

It was my turn to be quiet. The stereotyped image

of black men suggested that I should be randy, sexy and wild. But really I was quite shy and introverted – artists and writers might seem loud and jolly, but there had to be some space, some time to reflect on what has been seen and heard if events were going to be transformed into lines on a page. I loved Sylvie and couldn't have borne to hurt her; when you've been lucky enough to get the best, why bother about the rest? I pretended I hadn't heard Colette and began scribbling furiously at a sketch.

Not long afterwards Sylvie and I found a larger flat in Finsbury Park. My course ended and I devoted my time to painting. Sylvie had another book of poems published, and her small advance and royalties helped to pay the rent. Since the exhibition I'd had no trouble selling my paintings, but it took time to prepare and complete a canvas and materials were expensive. It seemed as though I'd have to get a steady job, perhaps in the glue factory, and paint at night.

Then one evening Alex came round carrying a bottle of wine, his face still streaked with clay from an afternoon spent working on the wheel. "You going tribal?" I asked, as I opened the door. He laughed and asked where he could wash. He came out of the bathroom looking cleaner, and we set the table.

"I want to talk to you about something," he said, playing with a fork.

"What is it?" I saw that he was looking a bit nervous. "Come on, tell me what it is? Do you want some money? We haven't got much, but you're welcome to a fiver."

"No, it's not that at all." He sat down and drew a deep breath. "Do you remember how we used to talk about making multi-cultural things?"

"Yes, I do. I designed some cards . . .'

"Well, I've had an idea. I'd like to work on my own account, with about three other people, making a whole range of things with multi-racial designs. I've got these four characters in my mind, one white, one black, one Indian, one Chinese. I've already done a few mock-ups. For example, there's these four people looking out of a window. There's another with a house where they stand on balconies, the figures lift out – it's for kids really – and for Christmas there's a candleholder with four different coloured angels surrounding the central candle, and at Easter . . .'

"Hey, hold on!" I told him, trying to slow him down. It was too much to take in at once. "You've really thought it out, haven't you? It sounds interesting. But where do I come in?"

"If you are interested, you'd come into the Print Section. Multi-cultural cards. You know, cards catering for the multi-racial society."

I could hear Sylvie getting the plates out. "I *am* interested. But how would we set it up?"

He relaxed now and swivelled a knife so that it spun round and round like a potter's wheel. "There's a studio shop nearby which we can rent. The owner's off to America for two years, but he may stay there and then we'd have first option on buying. It's in Palmerston Street, right on a main road. It needs some work doing to it, but the rent's quite cheap and I know we could make it work."

Sylvie brought in the rice and chicken and, while Alex opened the wine, he explained what we'd been talking about. "I think that's a great idea," she said. "It's relevant, to our lives, to everybody's life. It's worth trying."

"I've asked another couple of ex-students, Rashid and that Vietnamese guy, Hue, who does those beautiful wood-carvings. Perhaps it sounds fanciful, but I

97

can just see it, four friends producing the characters and the life we are living."

"What about money?" Sylvie asked him.

"Well, we've all got some money saved. If we all give as much as we can afford, we could buy equipment, and we'd run the shop together, no boss, shared profits."

"If any," I interjected.

"Well, I suppose I'm getting a bit carried away, but I just know it could work. I've done a bit of market research amongst friends, and there's quite a lot of interest. We'll have to go to auctions and buy an old kiln and a print machine, tables, chairs, counters and so on. I really want you to come in with me. You were the first one to give me the idea with your photograph of the children on the swings."

I laughed. "You didn't need much encouragement! If I said no, you'd have talked someone else into joining you."

"It wouldn't have been the same. I'm really excited about it, and I keep getting new ideas." He put his fork down and began riffling through his pocket. Bits of unfired clay fell on to the floor as he drew out scraps of paper covered with notes and sketches. Sylvie grinned at me.

"These drawings, you see, they're the other side. The side we know about is the death, the murder, the rape. But there is another side, the friendship, the caring, the helping. Everyone is beautiful." I looked at the drawings; they were very rough but I could see the four characters that he talked about in various situations, playing together in an orchestra, dancing down the street, cuddling each other's babies, leap-frogging.

Alex's idea, if it came off, would give me a chance to paint what I wanted, to break down the colour divisions that spelt only discrimination. We could reflect different images to the ones currently on display, the all-white, the all-black, the all-brown, reflecting the reality of our own lives. The idea of working in a group appealed to me. The artist's life is often solitary, and working with friends seemed attractive. We would take decisions together, refusing to perpetuate outmoded stereotypes. It was too late to put the black into the rainbow for Ma, but I had a responsibility to others as well.

Alex sipped his wine and asked, "Will you come and see the workshop with me tomorrow?" I looked across at Sylvie and nodded. She refilled our glasses and we lifted them simultaneously. I suddenly thought of Ma and the back of my eyes burned as I forced the tears down into my throat. Beauty in everything, Alex said. There is nothing beautiful in a gang of kids, marching, marching, marching down a road when they don't give a damn where they are going. I thought of Aunt Hanna lying stabbed in the street with her royal Ashanti blood staining the guttter. I remembered Danny, the months he'd spent at home suffering from agonizing headaches. There is nothing beautiful in fear.

Sylvie and Alex were smiling with a newborn hope. "To the new venture," Sylvie toasted us. The light caught our glasses and trembled there for a moment. Then they were empty.

16

We were sitting watching the latest riots on the news, a copy of the riot we had lived through: the bricks, the curses, the police, the hate. I couldn't imagine what was worse, political civil war when each side looked the same, so that the man approaching in the street might be a friend or an enemy, or racial civil war, when each civilian was a potential assailant, his skin his armour. Whenever I saw a skinhead swaggering along the road, boots tightly laced, head shaved, I knew him for my enemy. As we passed, we both sensed the hostility; he saw a black man, a nigger, a coon; I saw a Fascist, a honkey, a brute. Growing up in a racist society, we learned words that determined our actions. It was easier to beat up a wog, a Paddy, a Paki, a Yid than to harm a black man, an Irishman, a Pakistani, a Jew. Words lodged in our brain, dehumanizing others, and we ourselves were dehumanized by them.

A policeman was led out of the picture, his head streaming with blood. "It's almost impossible not to take sides," I said, "especially when the civil war is fought between black and white."

"But where does that leave Alex, who hates racism? Where does that leave me, with a black father and a white mother? What about me? What about you? How many of us can be sure that our blood is pure? The more I read, the more it seems obvious that there's no such thing as a pure racial group."

The fight was between master and slave, black and white, in our individual consciousness. Alex was offering a way out, a neutral territory, a total inclusion zone. The idea was that the workshop would supply multi-ethnic ornaments and gifts. Alex would produce ceramics and had already started making moulds to cast his designs. Hue would work in wood, and Rashid would make candles, jigsaws, bookmarks and so on. I was to design greeting cards. What would distinguish our work would be the four characters that Alex had described, the four friends of different origins appearing on each item. We wanted to be as flexible as possible, making seasonal items for Diwali, the Chinese New Year, Christmas and Easter, while providing a choice of gifts for birthdays, weddings, christenings and every major festival. We were devising multi-cultural diaries and calendars, listing the major feast days of the communities living in Britain, with a brief explanation under each one.

"I don't see how we can fail!" Alex said. "As far as I know, there's not another shop like this in the whole of England. However poor people are, they're always going to have to give presents at various times and the stuff we're going to provide will be great. At last the multi-ethnic society is being catered for!"

I hoped Alex's optimism would be justified. The other benefit of the scheme was that we could continue working at other outlets too – I could sell pictures independently of my work at the shop; Alex could finance himself by turning out pots. We had all found outlets in various places, Camden Lock market, small craft shops, galleries, so even if the venture failed, a possibility that Alex refused to think of, it wouldn't affect anyone's career.

We argued for sometime about a name for the shop, but eventually decided to call it Mixed Media. Having settled on a name, we began to clean out the workshop. Half of the area was already converted into a shop with a counter and shelves for display, the back room would be large enough to hold a kiln, a press and any tools and materials that Hue and Rashid would need. We painted the workroom white and hammered in cupboards. Sylvie came to help after work bringing a second-hand kettle from a junk shop and some cups so we could make coffee. It was agreed that we would supply our own materials till the shop was making money, then be repaid for outgoing expenses and draw money to buy what we needed. Any profits or losses would be equally shared.

We went off to auctions and bought a huge electric kiln and an Offset Litho machine fairly cheaply. We had all managed to contribute £500, earned by holiday work and selling pots and paintings. We had £1000 left to see us over the next few weeks. Things were getting complicated, and we realized that we'd need a book-keeper otherwise things would start to get out of hand. Sylvie volunteered to help as much as she could and said that if things went well, she'd come and work full-time.

I designed a sign blocking Mixed Media in clear letters and adding shadowing so that the lettering had a fairground effect. Beneath the words were four dancing figures, a black girl with a white boy, an Indian girl with a Chinese boy. Alex was delighted. "It's really striking," he said. "It makes you realize how little there is of this kind of thing. You know, I happened to see a cartoon strip in a paper the other day and one of the characters was black, the other white. It made me realize that I'd never seen mixed groups in cartoons before. It's awful, it's not till you see something for the first time that you realize you should have seen it long before. That's what this sign does to me."

"Let's hope it does it to other people as well,

otherwise we're going to need to have a bankruptcy sale!"

We had all been preparing goods for the shop for weeks and a few days before the grand opening Rashid brought his van round to collect our wares. Sylvie took a day off to help set them out. We put the cards on the revolving stands, the candles and other small ornaments on the shelves. Alex had made plates with his four figures embossed on them. We placed these, with Hue's carved figurines, in the window. Every item in the shop incorporated four different coloured people, holding hands.

A few people stopped to look in as we worked, a couple tried the locked door. We shrugged our shoulders and pointed to the notice which read: OPEN NEXT WEEK. I began to feel excited. What the four of us were doing was, I felt, relevant to us and to our contemporaries. Anyone who felt that something was very rotten in the state of England, yet who didn't quite know what to do about it, could now do something, although a very small something, by making a gesture and buying a token from our shop. We supplied the gestures in tangible form.

Alex had contacted the local paper and we got a good write-up with photographs of our work and a short biography on each of the craftsmen. There was a blurry picture of the four of us in the middle of the article. I had been printing posters to stick round the area, which said, "Mixed Media – Opening 12th October. A Multi-Ethnic Gift Shop – Something to Suit All Tastes." We went in on opening-day feeling very nervous and not quite knowing what to expect. Our goods were priced as cheaply as possible, and we could only wait and hope now. The hands of the clock moved closer to 9.30, then Alex cleared his throat, pulled his shoulders back, said, "Here we go" and opened the door. We were in business! A few customers were already waiting outside in the morning sunshine.

By mid-day we had to go and fetch some more boxes of stock. We were an instant success. We'd thought that we had made enough objects to last for months, at this rate they'd all be sold by Friday. "It might just be a flash in the pan," Rashid said disbelievingly. "Perhaps no one will come in tomorrow." But by the end of the week it was obvious that people were eager to buy our kind of work. We couldn't turn out enough.

That Saturday night Alex counted up the takings and told us there was a huge profit. Sylvie gave a week's notice to her firm and took over as manageress. We had to hire two assistants to serve in the shop. The queue for applicants stretched round the block. Remembering the fury of being sent away unseen from jobs herself, Sylvie interviewed everyone and picked those who seemed most committed to what we were doing. Safia could operate a till and Jenny packed the goods. The workshop at the back was so busy that sometimes Alex took ware out of the kiln, still hot, which was snapped up by waiting customers. I'd only made fifty copies of each of the first cards I'd designed, but these had been sold out by the second day. I stayed up all night reprinting thousands.

It was obvious that we'd have to expand. We hired a couple of youngsters, a black boy and a white girl, fresh from school, to help as apprentices in the workshop. This eased the pressure a bit and it felt good to be able to offer employment to people. All the staff took home the same pay at the end of the week, any surplus takings went into buying materials, equipment and paying the rent.

After two months we compiled a catalogue and opened a Mail Order Section, supplying items to people who couldn't come to the shop in person. We hired a young girl called Suyin to deal with this. Soon the exhausting rush of the first few weeks settled down into a steady stream and everyone relaxed. We had time to meet the customers, to talk to them and find out what they wanted.

One day I got chatting to a pleasant-looking man, who bought a dozen cards. "I'll show these to the lads at work," he said. "Where do you work?" I asked him casually. "I'm your local bobby," he replied, and laughed at my look of surprise. "We're not all Fascist pigs," he told me. "That's why I joined up. I want the police to be seen as fair to all people. It's not always easy. We get a lot of abuse in certain areas, and I know that some of the young policemen coming in are prejudiced. But I'm not, and a few of my colleagues feel like me."

Sergeant Jones came in several times after that, sometimes in uniform, sometimes off duty, to purchase gifts or·find out what new lines we were making. When I told Colette, she warned me that he was probably trying to put something over on us, but he wasn't. He was just a lone policeman trying to make dreams come true in another way.

Colette got a letter from Ras Peter. He had decided to stay in a Rastafarian community in JA and asked her to join him. By this time she was heavily involved in political activities and too committed to black issues in Britain to leave. She was also growing attached to Jimmy, though she would never admit it. I was glad that she'd decided to stay in England, we didn't see each other that often but I was happy to know that she wasn't far away. Colette was softer and kinder now, but sometimes when she was arguing she looked just like the young girl who had refused to put Calomine on her spots. Some of her

105

battles had been won, mainly on superficial issues, but even these were important. Black women could now buy cosmetics to suit their skin colouring in many chemist shops and, though this wasn't an earth-shattering advance, it did signify that the needs of black people were slowly being catered for, at skin level at least.

"Do you remember when you snatched my charcoal stick?" I reminded her one day. "Yes, I wanted to make talc for black people – it turned out grey!" Jimmy wondered what we were talking about. Colette told him and he roared with laughter. "You're lucky you weren't had up under the Trade Descriptions Act," he chuckled.

Colette smiled. I was glad she was going to stay, not for my sake alone, but because of the work she was doing. She was close to the young black scene, the kids who were involved in their own civil war, the one that took place in their minds. That was the worst war of all, the one that no one could fight for them.

17

After the publicity following my art exhibition and as a result of paintings that I was selling, I began to receive a few letters, some complimentary, some asking questions about my work, a couple of charity appeals and the occasional threat. The crank letters told me that I would die in ten days or be beaten up or castrated. I found it amazing that anyone would take the trouble actually to sit down and write such trash. Sylvie was worried but, when I continued in good health, we both treated the letters as idiots' tales, signifying nothing.

One morning I opened a tattered, grubby envelope to find a note from Dave. I hadn't seen or heard from him since the night of the Carnival riot. Dave sounded desperate and asked if I could send him £20 at an address off the Holloway Road. I was just about to write a cheque, when I put the pen down. Ma and Aunt Hanna had been old friends. I felt that I ought to follow Dave up personally. After work that evening I went off to find his house.

The streets were as dirty and shabby as I remembered. Most of the houses were unnumbered or had rusty name-plates so defaced that it was impossible to read the original sign. I found the house eventually by retracing my steps to the end of the road and then counting. I knocked on the door of an uncared-for tenement. No one answered. I checked the letter for the address – it was correct. I knocked again, and a woman with a white face streaked with dust pushed open a first-floor window and leaned out. "Yes?" she asked hostilely, fastening a button on her grubby nightdress, "What d'ya want?" "I'm looking for Dave, Dave Drysdale," I shouted up at her, feeling foolish. She leaned out of the window, her lank hair blowing in the wind. Pointing to the road, she yawned. "Right behind yer, mate!" The window was slammed shut.

I looked round. There was nothing behind me except for an abandoned rusty Ford Anglia that had been dumped by the kerb. I walked to the house opposite but saw with difficulty that the numbers on that side of the road were odd. Dave had written number six. Standing still for a moment to think what to do, I saw a wisp of smoke snaking out of one of the many holes in the car. I quickly crossed the road and rapped on a window curtained in newspaper. "Dave, are you in there? It's me, Phil."

The door was opened and I got into the driver's seat, wincing as the uncovered springs bit into my buttocks. The car stank of stale cigarettes, hashish, whisky and sweat. Retching, I mumbled a greeting. Dave's reply was slurred and incoherent. Turning round in the seat, I tried to peer through the darkness. He was stretched out on the back seat, his legs pulled beneath him, with a bottle on the back shelf and a tin of cigarette butts on his knee. He smiled at me with an effort and took another drag on the dog-end. "How long've you been here?" I asked. He started ramblingly to tell me that while Aunt Hanna had been in hospital, he'd been arrested again for burglary, and his father had refused to have him back home when he'd been released unless he promised to get a steady job and keep out of trouble. Apparently Aunt Hanna had made an almost complete recovery but was still weak, so Dave's father had to help around the house and saw no reason why his son shouldn't contribute financially to the household.

Unfortunately this attempt at Dave's reformation had come too late. Dave would never get a steady job. Having been allowed to spend his schooldays roaming the Brixton streets, he could hardly read nor write. Dave lived by his wits, duping the stupid, accepting from the generous. He was a natural hustler, not lazy, often the jobs he pulled required careful planning and figuring out. He was an intelligent guy who lacked the formal qualifications necessary for interesting employment. He would rather live in a car and raid dustbins for food and pick half-smoked fags out of the gutter than work in a glue factory, and I couldn't blame him for that. Dave had always been a slick operator, but being thrown out of his home had lost him his operations' base and he had taken to wandering aimlessly around London, squatting one night here, sleeping another night there, till he was locked into the cycle of failure that follows people who are dirty, smelly and hungry.

He had no permanent address, so he couldn't draw unemployment benefit. Besides he'd never worked. Most of his friends were either in prison or hiding from the law. After two months of tramping around he'd found this old car in the street and picked the lock. It was fairly comfortable; there was a selection of drinks in the glove compartment with some cardboard cups, a cushion rescued from a rubbish dump, a transistor radio someone had left behind in a coffee bar, and a few other objects dropped by careless pedestrians. "Parks are good places," he told me wisely. "You'd be surprised what people leave behind."

As he spoke, his stomach gave an agonizing rumble. "Wait there," I said. "I'll be right back." I got out of the car, stretching my legs and breathing in

109

gulps of the pure fresh air of Holloway. I'd never have believed that lead pollution could taste so good. Walking down to the grocer's shop on the corner, I bought a container of cooked chicken, bread, orange juice, milk, apples and cheese. Back at the car again, I knocked on the door and, when he let me in, the first thing I did was to remove the newspaper and wind down a window to let in some air. Dave grabbed the food, eating as though he had been on the verge of starvation. His hair was matted and dry, his dark skin flaking and patched with white, his eyes sunk into his head. "You always used to be so stylish," I reminded him. "You've really changed." The Dave I knew had been dressed in tapered suits, cut to show his firm thighs and lean figure. The Dave who sat behind me now wore old-fashioned grey trousers, soiled and torn, and a jumper and jacket three sizes too big. He'd stolen them from an Oxfam shop. Dave ignored me, too busy gnawing like a wolf at the chicken bone.

When he had finished his meal, he gulped down the orange juice and, reaching below the seat, drew out an old towel on which he wiped his mouth and hands delicately. Anyone would have thought that he'd just dined at Buckingham Palace. Refreshed by the food, he began to talk about the great life he used to lead, the clothes he had worn, the girls he had known, the dances he had been to, the goods he had stolen. Work in its traditional form was too boring for him. Dave wasn't going to work in an office and say, "Yes sir," "No sir," or in a factory, ruining his once manicured hands for £70 a week, when he could steal double that in half the time. No cat was going to get fat off his labour, except Dave himself. "You're not so fat now," I commented.

I asked about Aunt Hanna and the stabbing. He told me that in the aftermath of the riot gangs of youths had gone around attacking pedestrians who were a different colour from themselves. Aunt Hanna had been walking down the wrong road at the wrong time. Dave had been on a job over the river that day and, hearing the SOS, had returned to Brixton after visiting the hospital to organize a crowd of supporters in revenge. Some inspiration made him buy up all the plank wood in the local timber yard, and then his mates went around warning shopkeepers and householders that there would be another riot that night. When the frightened citizens tried to buy planks to board up their windows, they found it had all been sold. Then Dave and his friends came to the rescue, selling wood at double the price to grateful customers. He saw his mother's stabbing as a calamity of war, a war into which he had been born. And the fact that he had made money out of her calamity seemed only fair. "I bought her loads of flowers," he said disarmingly, "and she was ever so pleased."

Dave was one of the dispossessed, the alienated, the drop-outs, who lived on the fringes of society. He would rather live rough like an ancient Tom o' Bedlam, wandering from parish to parish, eating when there was food, tightening his belt when there was none, than become a wage slave. The slightest hint of authority stirred deep-down memories of plantation life; he refused to shackle himself to a time clock, or to lash himself with obedience. Dave was an urban knight of the road, accepting no law but his own.

"If you come to the shop tomorrow, I could fix you up with a job," I said. He looked trapped, hunted. "It's all right, you know, Phil. Just give me some Caesar to tide me over, man. Something'll turn up. I guess you're doing all right. I heard your name mentioned on the radio and I know about your shop."

111

"You could work for a week, get some money and find somewhere to live."

"I like this pad. Don't have to pay no rent and no one bosses me about."

There was no point in arguing. I gave him the money and the address of our shop and walked home, thinking.

I felt angry and discontented. Kicking an empty Coke tin that was in my path, I watched it skitter into the roadway spinning round and round till a passing car killed it. Outside a pub a gang of white youths were drinking and called insults as I approached. My hand tightened on the Afro comb I always carried in my pocket, but just as I drew parallel with them a young girl came into view and the kids turned their capacious intellects and pithy comments on her. There had to be something wrong with a society that offered the young the choice of hanging around doing nothing all day long, or working at some mind-deadening job in which no pride could be felt, no satisfaction gained. I'd often felt grateful that my gift for art had saved me from these two alternatives that seemed as bad as each other. I had no right to judge Dave for using his gifts for his own salvation.

A mouldy potato had fallen out of an overflowing dustbin, and two thin stray cats were squabbling over it. I remembered Colette practising carrying potatoes in a basket on her head and suddenly felt the loss that she had felt all her life. We had been taken from a traditional African unit in which each member of the tribe had an allotted task, helping his friends and being helped in return. Ras Ibrahim's teachings shone in the stars glimmering faintly above the North London squalor. The *tsotsis* who hung around the edges of life in big cities were the product of the industrial process that had created these cities. They relied on agility, intuition, their natural resources preserving the qualities that the rest of us had lost. Looking down at the wet pavement, I caught the rainbow of colour that shone in an oily puddle underneath a lamp-post.

Dave didn't turn up as I'd hoped he would the next day, but the following Monday he came along in his old bouncy manner, looking cleaner and fatter in a new suit, which I gathered he'd stolen from a market stall. We found him some jobs to do around the workshop and he actually stayed for two weeks, kneading the clay for Alex and preparing inks for me, but he constantly complained about the weight of the sacks and about how his new suit had been soiled or his hands stained. By the Friday of the second week he'd had enough. He disappeared soon after lunch, and when Sylvie went to make up the wages she found that £200 were missing. I was disappointed and angry at first, but, as Sylvie said, someone like Dave would hustle from his own mother, that was his life, his philosophy. "He's a predator!" she said sharply. Luckily I'd just been given some money for a painting I'd sold, so I put that into the kitty and we decided to forget the incident.

Not long afterwards we had to deliver some cards to a bookshop that was quite close to where Dave was living. Rashid drove the van and I asked him to wait for me while I went to see if Dave was at home. The car had gone. I knocked on the door of the house I'd first called at, and the same dirty woman in the same dirty nightdress looked out of the same dirty window. "'E got drunk," she said laconically. "'E was singing one of your jungle songs at the top of 'is voice and the plice come and towed the car away with 'im in it!" I

113

didn't bother making further enquiries. It was put down to experience.

Yet, ironically, I couldn't forget the image of Dave living in a car. I painted it; a battered rusty clapped-out vehicle, tyres flat, windows curtained with old papers and its inhabitant in tattered trousers and a dirty jumper, looking out of the broken glass with haunted eyes, like an animal peering from a lair. I called it "Night Side", for that's what Dave represented to me, the hidden part of our society, the tramps, the vagrants, the modern wayfarers whose fields have been turned into carparks. The car symbolized the built-in obsolescence of Western civilization, a man-made predator demanding eternal sacrifices – leafy lanes for concrete motorways, fields for parking-lots, human and animal blood for its libation.

Some months later the picture was bought and hung in the Museum of Modern Art. Dave wasn't given to going round museums, but I wondered if he'd ever see it and if he would recognize himself if he did. Strangely, I was paid £200 for this work, which I would have given to him had he not vanished. I don't consider that he robbed me, for just as he exploited me, I exploited him. Artists record other people's joys and agonies – we are predators too.

18

Dave was locked into a car that was going nowhere. I had sailed through the horrors and whirlpools of the deep and had reached my island. The shop was flourishing, I was working with my friends, Sylvie and I were happy. We lived simply, profits being ploughed back into equipment and new stock. When Sylvie became pregnant, I was filled with a sense of peace, of achievement, thinking that we would people our island with children. We went to the Register Office one morning and got married, with Colette and Jimmy as our only witnesses.

I wished that Ma had been alive to share our happiness, and began to remember things she had told me. How, for instance, when she'd first arrived in England she had seen the night frost steaming off fences in the morning sun and had almost called the fire brigade. I recalled the NO COLOURED, NO DOGS signs with which she had been greeted, and rejoiced that our children would not have to face those. But what would they have to face? Things that Sylvie and I had put up with, we would not accept for our own children. They would lie in our arms, soft and warm and innocent, and we would be their world, and we would have to explain and interpret that world to them. If they saw the world treating us unjustly, they would expect injustice too. From my island refuge I knew that the seas around were turbulent, seething, waiting for a hurricane to sweep them higher.

Colette and Jimmy came back to the flat with us. As we sat drinking coffee, Jimmy said plaintively, "I want Colette to marry me, but she won't. I envy you and Sylvie, especially now you're going to have a baby." "I'm not the marrying kind," Colette protested, "I will never get married!" Sylvie said afterwards, when they had gone and she was lying beside me on the bed, that she understood Colette. Marrying Jimmy would discredit her with the black movement. To have a white friend was one thing, a white husband was another. That was crossing the lines – joining the other side, even if that husband was on the same side as she was.

Colette was not the marrying kind. As she said, she was too much herself to need someone else to complete her. Some people come like that, self-contained. Marriage would only restrict and restrain her, and she needed all her energies to concentrate on the inequalities she saw around. There was never enough time to follow up all the stories to be covered, to answer the letters in her mailbag, or go to the meetings that required attention. I felt sorry for Jimmy, it was obvious that he loved my sister, yet she could not give him what he wanted.

Colette was like a candle, burning and vivid, and everyone knows what happens to moths.

Mixed Media had been supplying small shops in the locality with orders for some months. Now, with Christmas approaching, the top people's stores began to show interest in our work. We had many novelties, multi-racial angel mobiles, pottery children of different colours standing around a tree, wooden decorations, Rashid's painted candles in Alex's candleholders and my Christmas cards. Everything had a mixed ethnic group designed on it. We were even asked to open a branch in America, and export orders began coming in. We had to open another shop in Seven Sisters Road and take on more assistants. Once again we were working at full stretch. Our two apprentices were up-graded to craftsmen and we employed two more youngsters to fill their jobs.

Much of my original naïvety had been buried with Ma. When Sergeant Jones called round one night, I knew what he had come to tell me. A group of hooligans had assembled outside the shop that evening and smashed through the windows. It took us two days to sort out the mess. The attack didn't surprise any of us too much, but what we did find surprising and warming was the fact that the policeman turned up in his off-duty time to help us. We had to get new glass put in the frames. This time we ordered reinforced, shatterproof glass, with steel mesh shutters on the outside. The island was threatened. Every night, when work was finished the shutters had to be padlocked into place. I found padlocks menacing, like walls around a city, they signalled the fear within and the violence waiting outside.

We'd all been expecting an attack. We knew that no shop was safe and a place like ours was especially vulnerable because of what it stood for. Those who believed that good triumphs over evil were misguided. Evil had all the cards in its hand. Evil was strength, and could not be fought by being ignored. Evil threw bricks and forced us to defend ourselves. We were only surprised that our windows had survived for so long.

I asked Sylvie to stay at home – she was now heavily pregnant and tired easily, no longer as agile as she had been. She refused angrily, accusing me of patronizing her. Fragile as she was, she would not be pushed around by me or by a bunch of thugs. "When trouble comes, you've got to face it," she said crossly. "We're in this together, and we'll fight it together!"

In a strange way, the attack was good for business. Now customers felt brave when they entered the shop. They were participating in the fight, putting their money where their mouths were. I don't mean this in a sneering way; it was simply true. We all shared a feeling in those days, that we were being watched, that someone, somewhere, a Big Brother, was watching us and none of us knew why, or what party he belonged to, or what it was he wanted us to do. The name of this Big Brother was Terror, and he never slept or rested. Every knock at the door, every curse on the street, every whistle or fast-approaching car or mocking laugh belonged to him. The customers expressed this to us in different ways, saying, "You don't feel safe to walk the streets anymore," or "When I was young you didn't get this trouble," or "I don't know what the country's coming to, everyone's so tetchy and on edge." Buying from Mixed Media was one way of telling the unseen Enemy to get lost!

The atmosphere of fear made me become very protective towards Sylvie. I wanted to accompany her in the streets, to keep her always in my sight. As her belly swelled and she walked slower and more clumsily, I felt her vulnerability and could not bear to think of her alone, imagining terrible happenings if she was more than five minutes late. In civilized cultures a pregnant woman is treated with respect; in modern Britain I feared she would be beaten to the ground and trampled. Sylvie became sharp and irritable with me; she needed more space than I dared give her. I explained that the stabbings, the rapes, the murders, the riots had made me like this. I could not help feeling that the Enemy would get her too. One night, after she had snapped at me for tailing her like a detective, she suddenly kissed me warmly.

"I know why you're worried," she said, "but I'm not aiming to get killed. I know all about these streets and I've been worried for years. I've survived by learning where to go, where to shop, who not to look at, when to cross over the road."

That evening I drew her full-length picture, concentrating on her delicate cheekbones and rounded stomach. I painted her in a street with hands grabbing at her from all directions, feet shuffling from shadows trying to kick her down. I used Havannah brown for the face, touching it with white and copper highlights, her eyes black and strong and calm. The darkness of her hair was dimly visible in the lamplight. I called it "Pregnancy in Finsbury Park".

I was in the studio checking the ink level for a new printing run, when the phone call from the hospital came – Sylvie had been admitted and was in labour. By the time I arrived, the baby had been born. Sylvie was sitting up in bed looking beautiful; I held her tight and she clung to me. A nurse wheeled out a bassinet in which a pinky brown, wriggling black-haired baby was lying. "Pick him up," Sylvie said, but I couldn't move. I felt awkward and huge and clumsy, and my eyes blurred with the deepest emotion I have ever known. Sylvie leaned over and scooped the child up. She handed him to me and I held our son in my arms.

We couldn't think what to call him – at first we wanted to give him some splendid name to bear like a message. We came up with Shaka and Horombo, African kings of the past, but then thought they sounded too exotic for Finsbury Park. We toyed with Robinson and Columbus, but found them too colonial. In the end we chose Marc, in honour of Marcus Garvey – a plain, sensible name. Marc was a baby, a child in his own right, and we could not label him with our prejudices and policies. He would have to choose his own.

I left the hospital warm and glowing, and struck off through the darkness to walk home. That night I felt impervious, invincible. I was a father and joined by this experience to men of every colour, opinion, and creed. I was a Black Briton marching through the streets of my home town. A black man passed me and, as our eyes met in secret solidarity, he smiled. A white woman coming towards me gave me a friendly grin. Even the groups of skinheads and the crowd of young black kids waiting at the lamp-posts on either side of the road let me pass as though I was a king, and I accepted their silent homage and went by. Terror had gone home.

When Sylvie and Marc came out of hospital we had a small party in our flat for Colette and Jimmy and the staff of Mixed Media. Our friends had all brought presents for the baby. Rashid had made a rattle out of a bone with carved babies of every conceivable colour crawling over the surface. Hue gave a cradle, and Alex came with a tiny dinner-set with four laughing children of different colours glazed on. Colette gave Marc a soft wicker basket, made by an African friend, useful for carrying babies around. Danny came by with a bottle of Irish whiskey to wet the baby's head. Our little flat was full to bursting. The music was Indian, Chinese, Reggae, Heavy Metal. We drank to Marc and we drank to Sylvie and we drank to each other and to friendship and to peace and we really believed it. Marc slept in the corner within the cradle. Colette sat near him, holding his tiny hand. She looked sad, then caught my glance and smiled. I knew she was thinking about Ma and the way our lives had shaped. Putting my arm around her, I gave her a hug. "One love," I said.

"I like the name you gave him. Marc for Marcus, that's good. Ras Peter would approve."

"I'm glad you appreciate something I've done for once!" I smiled. She looked surprised. "Come on, Phil, I've admired your work for a long, long time." I felt surprised now. "But I thought you wouldn't approve of what we do?" "Look brother, you're trying to make a dream come true, and there's no harm in that. The people I deal with don't dream, I don't dream, we can't allow ourselves to dream. But I know that without people like you, without the dreamers, nothing will ever change."

It was impossible to discuss anything else with the music thumping in our ears. I turned the volume down and refilled everyone's glass. I was glad to have Colette's approval, her opinion meant more to me than almost anyone else's, even Sylvie's. But I didn't see myself as a dreamer. I thought of myself as a pragmatist. I went to look at Marc – for him I would try to be both.

"What kind of world have we bought you into?" I asked him silently. A racist world in which technology was destroying thousands of jobs a year, in which the earth's resources were being daily plundered, a planet whose air was systematically being polluted and whose seas were full of poison and whose tainted soil was full of chemicals. A world in which black children were taunted in playgrounds, or knifed in the streets. Above our heads satellites and the cast-off ironware of the space age went hurtling by, threatening to tumble on us at any moment, while skinheads waited to attack Asians on housing estates. "What can I offer you?" The love of possessions, the desire for power, the need for ownership in our overcrowded globe, in which we were all fighting for ever more scarce resources of food, shelter and land.

121

Marc stirred, his tiny amber fist waving in his sleep. Bending down, I tucked his tiny hand into the blanket. All I had to give him was sanity, vision, pride, resourcefulness, adaptability. The ability to see rainbows in oil-splashed pavements after a storm. He would have to find whatever else he might need for himself.

19

For the first few months of Marc's life I felt stretched and raw. I picked up, or imagined, insinuations and inferences that I had tried not to notice. I watched how people related to him, wondering what the passers-by who looked into his pram were thinking. Black women smiled and pinched his cheek, white women with thin pinched faces frowned as if to say, "Not another one!" Marc, however, was impartial to them all and smiled and blew bubbles into all faces with equal friendliness. He was so endearing that the black women would kiss his chubby, chestnut brown face and the strained expression of the white women would soften into a smile.

As new parents we realized how entrenched in tradition manufacturers were. There were few products for babies showing that those babies were part of a multi-cultural land. As we wandered round the shops, pink babies gurgled at us from tins of milk, pink babies were embroidered on dungarees, pink children romped over nursery wallpaper and appeared, laughing, on toys. Leafing through baby-care catalogues, we found one or two token black baby Britons, which hardly compensated for the vast majority of advertising and goods. I remembered Colette protesting about white creams and ointments. Now I began to sympathize. My baby was not invisible, but if society ignored him he, like others, might grow up to throw stones, to scream, to show that he existed.

Giving Marc his bottle while Sylvie rested one evening, I watched his cheeks sucking in and out, his brown eyes fixed on some private vision, half drowsing yet ready for a sudden noise. One year ago I had seen the world from my own standpoint. This tiny helpless pickney had changed my perceptions of and relationship to the world. I, as Phil Browne the artist, was strong. I could run, fight, climb, defend myself. As Phil Browne, father, I had to see the world through the eyes of a child, a black child.

As Marc grew older, Sylvie searched libraries and bookshops for stories to read to him. A few publishers had begun to cater for a multi-ethnic readership. Sylvie found a series of Anancy stories which she bought, but shelves and shelves in the bookshops were mainly filled with conventional fairy stories, featuring golden-haired boys and girls. I don't remember feeling deprived of black models when I was young, although my sister did. I must have grown up subconsciously accepting that I was invisible, that I did not deserve to have stories written about me, that I could only feature as servant or buffoon. Sylvie also vetoed books about helpless little girls who made Peter's sandwiches but weren't allowed to play football with him, which further restricted the choice. Some books for older children had black, or brown characters, but for babies we could find very little.

"We'll have to write our own books," Sylvie said, coming home exhausted and with one little volume to show for her efforts. "You can do the illustrations. You know, set them in our own neighbourhod, give them a realistic feeling, not always white kids in enormous gardens and posh houses, but pictures of black and white and brown children in streets like ours." Sylvie had changed too, she was more outgoing, more confident. She picked up a pencil and began jotting down ideas. We were both changing; it was as if Marc's birth had made us see things anew, presenting us with altered images, sharpening edges and lines that had become blurred with constant use.

I mentioned to Alex that there were few toys reflecting the changing society and we decided to fill the gap by opening a section for these in the shop. Not only would we emboss playthings with multi-coloured children, but we decided to research games from other countries and market those as well. When the department opened it proved a huge success. The public were avid for this kind of product.

"Its surprising how many people sit around grumbling and moaning because no one gives them what they want, when they could help themselves," Sylvie said, deftly changing Marc's nappy. The child clapped his hands in approval and we both laughed. Marc chuckled too. "I don't know why more people don't write books, if they can't find what they want and make things at home to sell instead of wasting their time and getting bored. There was a young lady in the shop this morning who complained that she'd been waiting for the Council to come and paint her house for three years. I told her to paint it herself. You should have seen the look she gave me!"

She sat Marc on her lap and gave him a banana. He squelched it between his fingers and sucked noisily. "It's the Great British Depression," I said. "It's like the fog and mist, it creeps into our body until the whole population is waiting for 'them' to come and fix it!"

"We're not like that!" she retorted. That was true. Somehow my friends had managed to avoid becoming fog-bound by apathy and were trying to shine a torch through the gloom.

* * *

When Marc began at nursery school, Sylvie returned to work full-time. Alex opened a café in the shop next door when it became vacant, selling Caribbean, Chinese, English and Indian food. We were very popular in the area, not only because of the goods we offered, but because we provided employment for several workers. Our turnover was increasing all the time and occasionally we invented jobs for people who were really desperate. Clients began to bring in their own designs for us to make up and that was great.

Alex had been proved right – he was altering people's attitudes and they were thinking multi-racially. I can see now that we were only a small finger in the dyke of separatism. Riots broke out on summer evenings, people withdrew again into their groups, social conditions worsened and the police learnt new methods of crowd control. But I couldn't see that then.

Marc came home one day, bruised and crying. Sylvie and I had both been waiting for it to happen, although we had never voiced our fears. A gang of white kids had punched and jeered at him, calling him blackie and nigger and telling him to go back to the jungle. Of course, we soothed and kissed him and told him what every black parent tells his child, that he was as good as whites, that he should be proud of being black, that lots of white people were nice and kind, like Uncle Alex and Uncle Danny, but Old Man Terror had touched our boy with his evil hand and from the time he was three until the day he would die Marc, like his parents before him, like every child in this forsaken country, would wait for the next time when someone would call him names.

I went to look for the gang and caught them hanging around a sweetshop. They were too busy trying to divert the shopkeeper's attention to notice me. I stalked up behind the biggest lad, shot out my arm and gripped his collar. He turned, frightened, to see who was attacking him. "You listen good," I hissed as I shook him. "You ever lay a finger on my kid again, or call him anything other than his name, which is Marc, and I'll give you such a hiding that you'll be black too!" "It wasn't me, mister," he whimpered. "It was her!" Contemptuously, I threw him down. Stumbling, he regained his balance, and the children were running, scrambling, as fast as they could go. I went home and told Sylvie that I was going for a walk.

My head was buzzing with a feeling of intense hatred. I'd learnt to counter racist jibes with an armoury of gestures – the cold stare, an indifferent shrug, a vague expression to indicate that I hadn't heard the word nigger, wog, bushman, Chocolate Drop. I cultivated a way of walking that warned people off. But one of Sylvie's friends had a son who'd been on a Youth Opportunities Scheme in a factory with another black guy and they'd both been so derided and humilated by their white workmates that they'd had to ask for sick leave. They were now unemployed, and I understood their need to throw bricks. At that moment, I felt like throwing bricks myself.

I walked for miles that night, steaming through the city unable to slacken pace. Electricity was flowing through my limbs, and all of it was plugged into fury. Some hours later I came to and recognized the street I was in. I'd walked from Finsbury Park to Notting Hill Gate and was standing in front of the house where Ras Ibrahim lived. I could see the light shining from his window and called his name. He leant out and smiled down at me, beckoning me to join him.

He offered me herb tea and lit his pipe, listening patiently as I stormed at him. "We're caught in a cleft stick! We stand out, we're different. The whites deride us, call us inferior, put us in ESN schools. If we react to their hostile treatment, we've got chips on our shoulders. If we don't, we're the typical black buffoon." I remembered little Enoka, sobbing in the playground with tears of angry frustration.

Ras Ibrahim breathed out a cloud of smoke. "Every black man is a Rastaman. InI carry Africa within." He would say no more but told me to go home to my wife and son. Feeling calm and strong, I left him. I caught a tube home, hoping that Sylvie would understand my absence. She came out as she heard my foot on the stairs and said, "You've been to see Ras Ibrahim!" "Are you psychic?" I asked. "No," she replied, taking my hand, "I can smell the ganja on your clothes!" We talked into the night, remembering names we had been called ourselves.

I realized that I'd been lucky. Because of my height I'd escaped a lot of hassle, and now I was working with friends, I could ignore the writing on the wall, the muttered comment. Sylvie had been much more affected by insults than me, but had learnt to deal with them by similar methods. It was hard for us to accept that our children would have to go through the whole dreary process again.

What could we give Marc to protect him, we asked ourselves? Legends from Africa, Ma's stories about Jamaica? Terrible tales of slavery that would make him shudder in amazement? I suffered for Marc what I had never suffered for myself. He was my touchstone, my drumbeat, quickening my awareness of the hidden reefs around. I felt that people became what they looked like, remembering the red-haired boy at school, who had always been quite placid until his friends tormented him, calling him Ginger, Carrots, Tomato-head, goading him into a furious temper by pulling his hair, and then saying that red-haired people were always quick to anger. The fat man was expected to be a clown, the thin man to be serious, the black man to be a mugger, the white man to be a judge. Marc, Sylvie, Alex came wrapped in their different coloured skins and were stereotyped accordingly.

Whereas I seemed to have been weakened by Marc's birth, Sylvie had become stronger. "We do have something to give him," she insisted. "Songs, dances, the way we move, poems and books and the things that we can make together. Mixed Media will help – it will open his eyes to new realities." We were trying to smash down the old labelling systems and institute new ones. Yet we were not deaf to the calls of repatriation, or blind to the BLACKS GO HOME signs. I began to peer painfully into the future trying to imagine what England would be like by the time Marc was a man. Questioning my island dream, threats and hopes I had long forgotten came flying back to me, doves with bricks in their beaks.

I transferred the anxiety I had felt during Sylvie's pregnancy to my growing son. When he went out to play in the street, I worried constantly until his cheeky face appeared again. I began to paint a picture, which eventually won a national comp-etition. I called it "Breaktime". Five white children stand around a hunched weeping black figure – the black kid's face full of humiliation and fear. Two dinner ladies, one black, one white, lounge with their backs to the group, drinking their tea. Some critics said that the picture was too biased and too stark, complaining that the artist implied only black kids were abused at school. I knew full well that all children bully, that black kids beat up white kids and white kids beat up brown kids, that black kids beat black kids and white kids beat white kids. But, as Sylvie said soothingly when I showed her the review, every time a white child is assaulted the incident is reported in the news. It was our child I was painting, our black son.

When the announcement of the award was made, Colette came round. Her face was radiant with pride, and she said it was the best thing I'd done so far. "You've shown what a few of us have felt for ages, that repression and corruption don't only happen in other countries, but in the Great Land of the Free. Most people don't want to accept that. They can put up with their grey tedious lives if they've got something to look up to. But now they're slowly beginning to see the corruption – they're reading of bent policemen, of whole squads found to be riddled with deceit. When allegations of beatings and harassment began, the white man couldn't believe it. He always said, 'It can't be true. Our police force is the best in the world.' But who said it was?"

"The newspapers said it was, and the television companies, and the broadcasting corporations," Sylvie answered.

"And who owns them?" Colette demanded, the beads dancing around her face, her eyes bright with anger. "Not the people who live on housing estates and whose homes are raided at dawn. Not the kids who are stopped in the street and searched when they are only talking to their friends or running errands for their dad. Not the husbands who return from the police station with broken arms! That's what you've shown me, Phil," she went on, turning the force of her gaze on me. I could understand why she was in such demand as a speaker. She was a born orator, and I'd been her first audience. "You've shown the helplessness of the powerless, the blindness of those in control." That was what I had wanted to portray. If we couldn't trust authority at school or the police force to deal justly with us, who could we trust but ourselves?

Blacknotes reported more and more Asian shops gutted and burned, black youth clubs raided and burnt, but no one was ever found to be guilty, no telegrams were received from Buckingham Palace expressing sympathy. The nameless ones walked tall and had no fear that they would be caught. No one could walk freely in the dark, except the murderers.

20

Marc finished his picture of a fire-engine. His face and sweater were covered in red paint. "I'm gonna be a fireman when I grow up," he informed me, sucking the end of his brush. I removed the brush and wiped him clean, running my hand over his black curls. Only the previous year the kids of Brixton had hurled rocks at fire-engines, shocking those to whom fire-engines were symbols of bravery and heroism. Colette had said that the fire service was one of the most discriminatory in the country. "There aren't many black firemen; to work with a team in danger you've got to have complete trust in your mates!" she had commented sarcastically.

Marc held up his picture for my approval. It was good, he'd captured the shape and dimensions of an engine, and had drawn himself climbing a ladder to rescue a lady holding a baby from the first-floor window.

"What colour will *our* baby be?" he enquired.

"Brown, like us!" I told him.

"Will it get hurt at school?"

"I don't know," I answered. "I hope not, but we'll have to teach it to fight, like you, just in case."

"What if it's a girl?"

"Don't let your mother hear you say that!" I said, smiling at him. "Whether it's a girl or a boy, we'll teach it judo, just like you.'

Sylvie was pregnant again and it was at this stage

of my life that I had serious thoughts of moving to Jamaica, where a black skin would be acceptable. Yet I had heard about immigrants being treated with suspicion. If they were successful, people were jealous. If they weren't, they were thought to be fool-fool. Sylvie wanted to stay in England despite the difficulties; she had no ties with Jamaica, and felt we had a lot going for us here. We had made it, in our own terms; we had changed things a little, and our children would have to learn to look after themselves as we had and perhaps change things a bit more.

Sylvie had more courage than me. I think it's a myth that men are braver than women. She tried to encourage me, saying, "Life is a struggle wherever you are. You have to fight for shelter, for food, for survival, for dignity, whether it's in JA, England, or Ethiopia. No one hands out these things. People work at jobs they hate, or can't find work, and it's the same everywhere." We talked it over, night after night. Africa, Caribbean, Britain, where did we belong? Ras Ibrahim's answer was, "InI belong to Africa." Enoch Powell replied, "Stay and there will be civil war!" England was not our spiritual homeland, but it was our home, and it had to be the homeland of our children.

I was worried too, about Marc's education. I could understand the reasons for black parents advocating the setting up of separate schools for their children. I knew a lot of black kids underachieved at school, but I had never worked out whether this was because they didn't want to achieve or because their teachers didn't expect them to. Colette had shown me stacks of reports written yearly since the 1950s, all saying the same thing and coming to the same conclusion. Black kids couldn't understand Standard English and were taught about white history and white geography and white culture, not their own. At school I'd tried to figure this out: if Colette and I could understand Standard English, if Indian and Greek and Chinese pupils could talk and write the language, why couldn't other black children? Did the people who wrote these reports believe that we were really inferior, or did they fail to understand that the Hopetons and Cliftons of the backrows saw education as a white-washing process?

The Moslem community was pressing strongly for separate schools where the Islamic ethic could be upheld. Blacks were arguing that they needed separate education. I viewed these suggestions with combined sympathy and horror. The sympathy was in recognition of years of failure and insensitivity and tactlessness on the part of the Education Authorities. The horror came when I thought about the effect of separate schooling. In Northern Ireland there were schools for Catholics and Protestants. In Cyprus there had been schools for Turks and Greeks. In Israel there were separate schools for Arabs and Jews, and there was no meeting point, socially or culturally, for the children in those countries. The only time they met was at either end of a gun. I thought of South Africa. Separate schools spelt apartheid to me. The world was made up of many colours and I wanted my children, like me, to enjoy the variety.

I puzzled over this problem and sent for some leaflets from the High Commission. I also wrote to the headmistress of one of the few all-black schools in London and read the prospectus she sent. If Marc went to this school, he would learn about the black heroes and heroines of the past, about Mary Seacole instead of Florence Nightingale, about African and Caribbean culture, the songs and dances of his ancestors. His teachers would expect the best of him, not the worst. What he would not learn was how to mix with white children, how to stand up in the society in which he had to live. We could teach him pride at home, we could read him legends and tell stories and take him to places where he would see black art and culture.

"We should send him to the local primary school," Sylvie insisted. "If he's bullied, he'll have to learn to live with it and fight back. Don't you think they bully each other in black schools?" We were mounting an exhibition at the Commonwealth Institute and I was designing new prints. I felt hypocritical, preaching multi-racialism, while doubting it could happen. I had to hope that like me, like Sylvie, like Colette, Marc would take what he needed from school and reinforce it with information from home, adapt it to his own situation.

Finally we put his name down at the local school as Sylvie had suggested. "Multi-racialism *is* happening," Sylvie said to me as she filled in the form. "We are making it happen. Look at our friends, they come from all over the world, they are white and brown and black." That was true. I had been best man at Danny's wedding. Alex and Lynda, Rashid, Hue and their girlfriends were constant visitors. Yet it was not my friends that worried me. It was the Enemy. Terror, always waiting round the corner, ready to throw stones, to taunt, to kill. I wanted my children to be safe. Sylvie folded the form and put it in the envelope. Then she sat back, her hands on her rising stomach. "You can't give a child safety. All you can do is give it courage."

We called the new baby Dawn. Alex brought round food from the café and our friends filled the house with flowers and presents. I held Sylvie's hand, thinking to myself that she looked so young in her deep red dress, her face glowing bronze in the soft light.

She put her arm round my neck and pulled my face down. "I love you, Phil," she told me. "Look around. Look at the people in the room. Aren't I right about what I said?"

Colette came over, cuddling the baby to her, while Jimmy brought her a drink. "It's about time you became a mum," Sylvie said. Colette frowned. "When I see little Dawn, I feel I'd like to be a mother, but I don't think I could allow myself the luxury . . . There's so much to do, so much to change." She put the child in the cradle and took her drink. Then she burst out, "How can I have a child, when I want to change the world! A baby would take my mind off things. It would muzzle me. They're always waiting at my back and with a tiny child, I'd be so vulnerable. I would be scared to shout so loudly, to say what I mean. I know that my name is on files, at the police station, in right-wing organisations. If I die, that's it. If I have a child, I would die many times."

The room was hushed, guests trying not to look in our direction, embarrassed. Rashid quickly put on another record and everyone began moving again. I touched Colette's arm. "You can share our kids," I reassured her, smiling. "Any time you want to baby-sit, don't be shy to offer." She grinned back, grate-fully. "That's a deal. I'll try to come over more often, be more of an auntie to these two." She looked wistfully at the sleeping baby and bent over to kiss Dawn's cheek. When she straightened up, I saw that the child's face was wet.

Colette's speech had made me realize how very lucky I was, at home and at work. Sylvie's poems and my pictures were opening people's eyes, finding acceptance and even fuelling schemes for change. I had a partner with whom I'd found peace and I knew the wonderment that came when a tiny baby nuzzled its head into my shoulder, or smiled when I came into the room. The few irritations were so minor as to be easily dismissable: the graffiti on the metal shutters outside Mixed Media, the occasional threatening letter, the odd disagreement at work.

A month after Dawn's birth, Colette and Jimmy came to stay for the week-end and on the Saturday night I took Sylvie to see *Countryman* at the Classic. We were both excited. We hadn't been out together for months and reports of the film were excellent. After the show we were going out for a meal. "Might as well be extravagant for once," Sylvie told Colette. "I'll bring you back a patty." "Great!" Colette's face lit up in a big smile. "Make sure there's plenty of pepper sauce on it. I like it hot!"

We had a smashing evening. The film was set in Jamaica and starred a Rasta superman performing athletic miracles and defeating his enemies. The soundtrack by Bob Marley, Toots and the Maytals was terrific. The scenery was beautiful, and I recognized landmarks that Ma had told me about.

After the show we went to eat and returned home in a taxi, feeling like aristocrats. Sylvie had wrapped some cakes in a serviette to give to Colette and Jimmy and a spicy smell perfumed the cab. As we turned into our street a thud of terror hit my stomach. The driver jerked on the brakes with an oath. "Christ, I can't get through there, what's bleeding going on!" Fire-engines and police cars were parked all over the road. Sylvie had wrenched the door open and was running down the street, shouting something I couldn't catch. I chased after her, the taxi-driver tore after me. We pushed our way through the crowds to find our house, or the remains of it, smouldering while hoses played on the burning embers. Sylvie was screaming. The taxi-driver held her tightly round the shoulders, saying, "It's all right, love. It will be all right!"

A neighbour struggled towards me, his hands blistered. "Philip, oh God, Philip." Tears were streaming from his eyes. "She managed to get the children out – we all tried to get to them, to help. I caught the little one – oh God." "Where's Colette?" I bellowed. "Is she still in there?" I tried to break through the cordon, which was stupid, because the top floor had gone, and Colette and Jimmy must have gone with it. Countryman would have torn his way through the line and flown up to the top of the house and found his sister and her friend alive. I wrestled with the firemen but they held me back, two on each side. I nearly broke away once but they held me again, trying to explain in words I couldn't understand that it was no use, everything had been done that could have been done. "Colette, my sister, Jimmy, I've got to save them!"

A tall detective came over to me. "Are you Philip Browne?" Sergeant Jones appeared behind him and grasped me by the arm. "That's Philip. He's the father of the children." The detective cleared his throat and wiped a hand over his brow. "I'm very sorry to have to inform you that we have reason to suppose that the two adult bodies we have removed from the wreckage are the remains of your sister and a friend. Thankfully, your children have escaped, unharmed. They have been taken to hospital for a routine check-up, but they should be released tomorrow."

As he finished speaking, the burning skeleton of the house collapsed and sparks flew upwards into the sky. Someone was howling like an animal in the middle of the street. Police and firemen and spectators were drawing back to leave him howling beast-like in the road. Someone was howling with the agony and sorrow of his capture and his slavery.

Colette, Colette, where are you now? Colette, Colette, where have you gone? Colette, Colette, why have you left me? Then a doctor shoved a needle into my arm, and the howling stopped.

21

Do you think that when man colonizes space things will be better up there? Do you think that all space men will be equal, standing together to conquer the unknown? Will they have a classless society? Or will space too have its rich and its poor, its white and its black, its haves and have nots?

I asked myself this question, over and over again. It seemed strange to me that in the twentieth century people could not walk the streets without fear. It seemed strange to me that in the twentieth century mothers got stabbed and sisters burnt to death. It seemed strange to me that in the twentieth century young men were mugged at street corners and folk dared not go out at night in case their house was not there when they returned. It seemed strange to me that people still believed in a benign and munificent god when, in the twentieth century, all these things still happened.

Alex and Lynda looked after us. When we began dully to look around again, we saw that we were in their home above the workshop. The children were unscathed – Dawn was too young to remember anything and Marc had woken briefly to find himself in a fireman's arms. It had been an adventure to him. We had to explain that Colette had died, but I don't think he related this to the fire. The police suspected that a petrol bomb had been thrown through the window and asked if any threats had been received. I told them about the occasional threatening letters we had received, but we had thrown them away. The arsonists have never been caught.

I cannot remember much about the following months. People called to interview me about Colette – I answered them vaguely, distantly. Someone asked if I had any pictures of her; the only thing that had escaped the fire was an old iron box in which I kept my most personal drawings. I showed him the sketch I had made when Colette was a schoolgirl, drawn on the back of a cornflakes box. He offered me a vast sum of money for it, but I refused. The picture, slightly scorched, now hangs in our hall, a tribute and a memory.

We sat, Sylvie and I, in Alex's home, looking at the walls in silence. Friends came to mourn with us, Danny, John, Sergeant Jones, even the taxi-driver found out where we were staying and brought with him Sylvie's shoulder bag, which she had left on the seat of his cab. As she opened it the stale cakes fell out and she started sobbing. We got up, we dressed, we played dutifully with our children, but we had ceased to exist. Then slowly life began to return; we noted that it had rained or the sun had shone, that Dawn had cut a tooth or Marc's scab had fallen off. One day I found myself in front of a canvas. My hands reached automatically for paint and brushes. By the end of the day the canvas was covered with a picture of a burning house. After this, I gradually returned from the Inferno.

We found another flat and moved in, helped by our friends who gave us items of furniture. This flat was larger than the first and had a small garden. We converted half of the dining-room into a studio. Sylvie was quieter than before, but outwardly our lives went on. The children helped us, unknowingly. We had to play with Marc or take Dawn to the children's playground in the park when, on another level, we were kneeling at the gravestones in our minds.

Late one night there was a knock at the door. We stiffened nervously. Who was coming to attack us now? The knock was repeated, urgently. Taking a kitchen knife, I opened the door. A large black figure stood blinking in the light from the hall. "Ras Peter!" I exclaimed. "Come in!" "One love, Jah," he grinned at me, clasping my hand. "I had such trouble finding you. Where is Colette?" I could not speak. Sylvie drew him into the room and told him what had happened. Ras Peter swore, raved, cursed. We made up a bed for him on the settee, and he sat up all night smoking ganja and muttering to himself, "Burn, Babylon, burn!" I sat up and watched with him, silently. In the morning Sylvie found us there, Ras Peter still muttering, "Burn, burn, burn." "There's been enough burning," she said coldly.

Something had happened to Ras Peter during our private wake. "I have done with this land and with waiting," he told us. "I am going to Ethiopia now. You come too!" "How will you get there?" Sylvie asked. "Jah will provide." I glanced at Sylvie. Marc came running into the room and Ras Peter lifted him on to his lap. For a moment I was tempted to take my family and get out of this place, this hell, but then I came back to reality. There was no Ethiopia for me. "I am going to get the dust of Babylon from my heels. Haile Selassie is telling me to come," said Ras Peter. "Haile Selassie is dead," Sylvie remined him curtly, but Ras Peter didn't believe in death. He blessed us and was gone.

He did get to Ethiopia. He stole a van, took it across Europe and drove to Spain. There he sold the vehicle and with the money crossed to Morocco, travelling eastwards till he reached the Ethiopian border. He took the dust of Africa in his hands. He had returned, the exile, to Zion. But Ras Peter had reckoned without the long hand of Interpol. In the midst of his rejoicing he was arrested by the Ethiopian police. He argued and prayed but was thrown into jail. I got a letter from him, begging me to come and rescue him. He was Colette's friend, she had told me she loved him because he was free, because he had what we did not have. I sent him some money, enough to return to England or go wherever he wanted. I don't know where Ras Peter is now, I have not seen him since. I wonder if he ever got out of his Ethiopian prison or if he is wandering over Africa, searching for his lost roots. Maybe he is in a Jamaican commune, praising Jah. I hope that he is in Africa; I see him in my mind's eye wandering like a *griot* of old, from village to village, entertaining the villagers with tales and received with courteous hospitality.

I went back to the shop. My colleagues greeted me with embarrassed glances and awkward silences at first, but after a couple of weeks the atmosphere returned to normal. I still felt removed and separate from the busy life around me. Exhausted – I have since read that this is a reaction to grief – when I got home, I often fell asleep as soon as I sat down. Sylvie had nearly recovered from the fright of almost losing the children, but would never leave them at night.

I was half-dozing one evening after a day spent working on a new print in which children danced around a tree, each with a flower in their different coloured hands. I had worked half-heartedly, cynically, thinking when they are older, this hand will throw a petrol bomb, this hand swing a chain. The radio was on low. Someone was singing about Love and Harmony. Then a newsflash cut through my stupor. Scrap-dealers had landed on an island in the

South Atlantic. The music continued and I slept again, dreaming of Colette and Ma. Then I woke up again to hear the same news being broadcast. Sylvie had finished putting the children to bed and was now sitting opposite me, writing in her notebook. I saw her puzzled face as the bulletin continued. The Falkland Islands had been invaded.

We found an old atlas, but didn't know where to begin looking. Sylvie thought the islands were off the Scottish coast, I plumped for Norway. At last we located them, half an inch from the Argentinian mainland. "How can they be British," Sylvie asked me, "when they are so far away?" She measured the distance with her hand. From Britain the islands were two handbreadths, from Argentina a thumbnail away. "The Foreign Office must have made a mistake," she said. "It's a farce. No one will go to war."

As I walked to work the next morning, the news stands were full of posters: ARGIES ATTACK SOUTH GEORGIA. People in the streets were talking in bemused terms about the invasion, a few militantly, spoiling for a fight, most wondering what the fuss was about. On the radio we heard that Public Opinion was solidly behind the Government's stand, but, as Alex had explained at Art College, Public Opinion was a myth. No one really believed it would come to a battle.

It came to a battle. Alex began to look worried, the ship that his brother Matthew was serving on had been sent to the war zone. Alex was quieter than usual, heaving the clay on to the plaster slab and pounding it with great savage blows. "What's the point?" he muttered to himself as the clay hit the slab. "What's the bloody point of it all?" An announcement came over the old radio we kept in the workroom, praising the courage and devotion to duty of the troops who were sailing off into their sunset.

"Duty!" Alex exploded. "None of those kids realize what they're doing. They never do. They'd never even heard of the Falkland Islands until last week. Most of them are like Matthew, faced with perpetual unemployment or a spell in the Services!" He smashed the clay down again as if he had the entire War Office under his fist.

I tried to calm him. "Relax, Alex, I'm sure Matthew will be all right. It's no use your working yourself up. That won't help. Why don't you take the rest of the day off, go for a walk with Lynda or something? But don't go mad, that's no good. I should know, I've just come back from all that!" His shoulders sagged and he turned to me, putting his hand on my shoulder. "Hell, I'm sorry, Phil. When I think what you've been through . . .'

"Listen," I told him, "you helped me through that, and I'll help you through this." I didn't know what else to say. The words sounded stupid in my ears, but Alex turned back to the clay.

The letters in the press grew angrier as the war continued. "Let the dagoes have it! Show them we mean business!" "We must fight for freedom!" "Get in there and give the Argies hell!" "Teach them a lesson! It's ours!" According to the loyal press the battle would be easily won. But the struggle turned out to be longer and bloodier than anyone could have imagined. Soldiers were mobilized and killed on both sides, ships sunk, fighter jets brought down.

In my weekly copy of *Blacknotes* there was a leading article, reminding readers of the incident of Diego Garcia. This British-owned island in the Indian Ocean had been requested by the United Stated as a military base. The British Government had been pleased to comply, but first of all the 2,000 islanders had to be removed. They had not wanted to leave, and had been shipped against their will to Mauritius where they were now living in poverty. The islanders were all black.

Blacknotes then posed the question, what would have happened had the Falklanders been black, would the troops have gone in then, or gone in so quickly? And I asked myself the question, what would I do if I were to be called up? Ma used to say, "Thief from thief, God laugh!" meaning that if robbers steal from each other if doesn't really matter. Argentina and Britain were sending young boys to struggle over a couple of windswept rocks for honour, for principle, for patriotic pride.

Wars, like riots, redefine attitudes. I was not going to fight for second-class citizenship, for disproportionate unemployment, to be stopped unnecessarily on the streets, for unwarranted harassment. I might fight for a Land of Heroes, but never for a country of thugs. I would not fight for the Old Order, for the Old Order had burnt my sisters, murdered my brothers, ignored or insulted my son. Britain was fighting, so our leaders informed me, for freedom, human rights, and democracy, yet thousands of citizens in the Land of the Free found only discrimination, hostility, aggression. My only interest in the war was a personal one, my own island had already been invaded, my control threatened, my territorial rights violated. From now on I would fight only for my family and myself.

Matthew's ship was hit by a guided missile system that Britain had supplied to the right wing Fascist dictatorship twelve days before the outbreak of hostilities. Alex and Lynda waited anxiously for news, and then heard that Matthew was one of the wounded survivors. Some weeks later he was brought home and taken to a military hospital, his right arm

146

shattered and useless. When he was discharged everyone did their best to comfort and encourage him, but Matthew, the boy who had worked so delicately on circuit boards and who had played the violin, took his disability badly. When Lynda returned from work one evening she found him dead, an empty bottle of sleeping-pills by his side and the gas full on.

Suddenly everything seemed clear. It began with a sense of self. I'd felt mad because of what I and my people had suffered and then arrogant *because* I had suffered. I'd met others of my group who were as mad and as arrogant as me because they had suffered what I had. We felt mad and arrogant together, saying that no one else had the right to feel as bad as us. Then we heard of others who felt equally mad, claiming that no one had ever been treated as cruelly as they had. Indian untouchables, Jews whose families had been killed in concentration camps, an Irishwoman whose people had died in the potato famine, an Englishman who was tortured in a Japanese prisoner-of-war camp. All these people were in groups with their own madness and arrogance.

Slowly I came to see that all these seemingly unrelated madnesses were the same anger. We had all been transported by the Puppet Master, spurned by the same people, scorned by the same élite which controlled our lives. The Puppet Master had many names, Power, Greed, Territory, Money, Politics, The Good Life, and in order to maintain his position he had to keep us all apart, fighting each other, the white against the black, the English against the German, the Protestant against the Catholic, the Hindu against the Moslem, lest we, the puppets, united together and destroyed him.

The only way that I could attack the Puppet Master

was by trying to unite communities, broaden horizons, painting images of black and brown and white and umber together. I could attack the Puppet Master with paintbrush and paint, and I somehow knew that I would win.

22

The Lost Ones. I paint them groping blindly, all around me, the young. The sign on their shield is a hand, two fingers pointing upwards in a gesture of contempt. They have a strange ugliness, black, white and brown. With their shaven heads, with their empty eyes, they seem to have come from another planet. They have no jobs. They are tall and strong and restless, violent and rude and threatening. They hunt in packs at street corners and along alleyways, favouring dark shadows. Abusive, abrasive, barbarians. They are without a past and without a future, and they are numerous and evil. One thing separates them from other generations. They never smile. I reflect that smiling is a particularly human expression. These spawning youth are the first link in a genetic chain that will lead backwards into Chaos. Mankind has destroyed its planet and those of us who remain wait for our final extinction. Perhaps a new form of life will evolve from the ruined earth free of human faults, to live in peace and happiness.

I finish my picture and look at the street below. I see other youths, their eyes filled with joy and hope as mine once were. Their laughter rises freely into the air. One hope, one aim, one destiny. Keep the faith brother. I have to keep faith with them. I paint them too, edging their smiles with gold.

* * *

It was Dawn's first birthday. Our friends were gathered round the table, smiling and eating and joking. Scraps of wrapping paper lay littered over the floor and the children were playing with Dawn's presents. Alex, Lynda, Danny, Rashid, Hue, John and their wives and girlfriends and kids were all there. The rain stopped and the sun came out, shining strongly and warming the room with its radiance, gilding the crumbs of birthday cake.

"Can we go into the garden?" asked Marc, and the children started jumping up and down. They ran out laughing into the light. I held Dawn in my arms, so she could see them through the window.

Sylvie had planted flowers in the small yard and they were opening out in the spring. The children ran, dancing and tumbling on the damp grass. The earth is the Lord and the fullness thereof. Dawn chuckled and clapped her hands. The children were playing a ring game now, walking round and round in a circle, chanting a jingle. Here was the card I had designed so listlessly, come to life. Dawn pointed to the sky. I saw a rainbow shaded from dark to light, framing the scene. And one of the colours was a grey so dark that it was black.

Sylvie came and stood behind us, her arms around my waist. I heard the murmur of the adults as they cleared the table. I closed my eyes for a moment and when I opened them the rainbow had faded. But I had seen it and Dawn had seen it too. She pointed again, asking to go into the garden. I set her down and, with Sylvie holding one hand and me the other, she toddled uncertainly into the garden as we led her out to her friends, the black, the white, the brown, the golden, and they ran to her welcomingly and held her safe.

150

ALSO IN

Graham Greene The Third Man and The Fallen Idol; Brighton Rock

Thomas Hardy The Withered Arm and Other Wessex Tales

Rosemary Harris Zed

L P Hartley The Go-Between

Ernest Hemingway The Old Man and the Sea; A Farewell to Arms

Nat Hentoff Does this School have Capital Punishment?

Nigel Hinton Getting Free; Buddy; Buddy's Song

Minfong Ho Rice Without Rain

Anne Holm I Am David

Janni Howker Badger on the Barge; Isaac Campion

Linda Hoy Your Friend Rebecca

Barbara Ireson (Editor) In a Class of Their Own

Jennifer Johnston Shadows on Our Skin

Toeckey Jones Go Well, Stay Well

James Joyce A Portrait of the Artist as a Young Man

Geraldine Kaye Comfort Herself; A Breath of Fresh Air

Clive King Me and My Million

Dick King-Smith The Sheep-Pig

Daniel Keyes Flowers for Algernon

Elizabeth Laird Red Sky in the Morning; Kiss the Dust

D H Lawrence The Fox and The Virgin and the Gypsy; Selected Tales

Harper Lee To Kill a Mockingbird

Julius Lester Basketball Game

Ursula Le Guin A Wizard of Earthsea

C Day Lewis The Otterbury Incident

David Line Run for Your Life; Screaming High

Joan Lingard Across the Barricades; Into Exile; The Clearance; The File on Fraulein Berg

Penelope Lively The Ghost of Thomas Kempe

Jack London The Call of the Wild; White Fang

Bernard Mac Laverty Cal; The Best of Bernard Mac Laverty

Margaret Mahy The Haunting; The Catalogue of The Universe

Jan Mark Do You Read Me? Eight Short Stories

James Vance Marshall Walkabout

Somerset Maugham The Kite and Other Stories

Michael Morpurgo Waiting for Anya; My Friend Walter; The War of Jenkins' Ear

How many have you read?